MATHEMATICS

Statistics
Unit S1

COLEG GWENT
PONTYPOOL CAMPUS
BLAENDARE ROAD
PONTYPOOL
NP4 5YE

Dr I G Evans

AS/A LEVEL

WJEC AS/A Level Mathematics
Statistics Unit S1

Published by the Welsh Joint Education Committee
245 Western Avenue, Cardiff CF5 2YX

First published 2001
Second publication 2002

Printed by Gwasg Gomer
Llandysul, Ceredigion, SA44 4QL

ISBN: 1 86085 458 3

PREFACE

The prime aim of this text is to provide sound coverage of the syllabus content of Unit S1 in the A/AS Mathematics scheme of the WJEC. It is envisaged that the text will also be appropriate for the corresponding specification of other examining boards.

Chapter 3 (Probability) is identical with Chapter 1 of the text that was written for Module S1 and Chapter 4 (Discrete Random Variables) consists of a selection of the relevant topics in Chapter 2 of the Module S1 text. Chapter 1 (Sampling Methods) and Chapter 2 (Descriptive Statistics) are new topics at this level but are included in the National Curriculum.

As in the text for Module S1 each chapter here has been sectionalised with each section covering a particular topic followed by worked examples and exercises to illustrate the methods introduced. Each of Chapters 2, 3 and 4 end with a set of miscellaneous exercises on the topics covered in a chapter, those at the end of Chapters 3 and 4 consisting of questions from past papers set by the WJEC.

At the end of the text you will find numerical answers to all the exercises and an index.
The binomial and Poisson tables used in the worked examples in Chapter 4 are those in *Elementary Statistical Tables* previously published by RND (Cardiff) but now being published by WJEC. Students using the approved set of tables in *Statistical Tables* by Murdoch and Barnes (published by Macmillan) will need to modify the given solutions of the worked examples requiring the use of tables.

Every effort has been made to produce a text free from errors. If you should come across any that have escaped our attention it would be appreciated if you would kindly inform the author or the WJEC.

CONTENTS

Chapter 1

Sampling Methods

1.1 Population and Sample

A statistical investigation is one designed to obtain information on some specific characteristics (variables which may be qualitative or quantitative) of a collection of items. The collection of interest is referred to as the **population.** Whereas we are familiar with the term 'population' as meaning the collection of people in a region (e.g. town, county or country) the term has a wider interpretation in Statistics in that the items in the population may be people, plants, animals, farms, supermarkets, mass produced articles, and so on.

An investigation which obtains the required information from every item in a population is called a **census**. The U.K. Office of Population Censuses and Surveys (a government agency) conducts a census of the U.K. population every 10 years, the next one being due in 2001. In this census the population of interest consists of all households in the U.K. In the census held in June 1991 every head of household was required to supply information on a variety of matters. The government uses census data to help in the formulation of policies for the future conduct of the country. It is evident that this census is a mammoth task and, despite the advances in computer technology, there is a considerable time-gap between receiving the data and publishing the results.

A less demanding census is one where the population consists of all the pupils of a particular school, for which possible variables of interest might be age, form year, weekly pocket money, time spent per week watching television, having a pet animal, and so on.

The government has sufficient resources (cost-wise and time-wise) to conduct the ten-yearly census, but other organisations are not as fortunate. When a census is ruled out because of the cost and time involved, the investigator will have to be content with obtaining the required information from a subset of the population. The items in the chosen subset are referred to as a **sample** from the population and the investigation is referred to as a **sample survey.** In the particular case where the population consists of people and the variable of interest is an expression of opinion the investigation is referred to as an **opinion poll**, the most common of which are those held by various organisations prior to a general election in an attempt to predict the outcome of the election.

Note that sampling is unavoidable in a situation whereby the required information on an item can only be obtained by destroying the item as, for example, when investigating the lifetimes of electric light bulbs or batteries.

Sample surveys are commonplace these days and the results obtained are readily available in the press and other media. Published data by the government on such things as unemployment and inflation are based on sample surveys. The Consumer Association, the publishers of *Which?* magazine, conducts sample surveys of its members on a regular basis, one aim being to compare different brands of a product and to recommend a "best buy".

Since the purpose of a sample survey is to obtain information about the population, it is clearly desirable that the sample is truly representative of the population being investigated. A good example is a blood sample taken from a patient since it is reasonable to suppose that the patient's blood is consistent. However, this is not the case in practical situations of the type considered here. An obvious requirement when selecting a sample from a population is to avoid **selection bias,** which occurs whenever the sampling is such that some items in the population are more favoured than others. It has been established that a selection process based on human judgement is very likely to be biased even though the person making the selection may not be doing so purposely. For example, consider the situation in which a person is asked to remove a handful of coins from a bag containing a large number of coins of varying denominations. The likelihood is that the selected coins will be predominantly the larger ones (in size).

The safest way of eliminating selection bias is to have a mechanical procedure that will ensure that every possible sample of the specified size has the same chance of being selected. Such a sample is likely (but not guaranteed) to be representative of the population. Such a procedure is referred to as **simple random sampling,** which is described in the following section when the population is finite and the items are available on a numbered list.

Exercise 1.1

1. Explain briefly the main advantage and the main disadvantage of a census as compared with a sample survey.

2. Why is it advantageous to have a sample that is representative of the population?

3. A teacher requires a sample of 5 pupils from her class for some specific purpose. She chooses the 5 who are sitting in the front row. Suggest a possible variable that can be associated with pupils for which the selected sample is clearly not representative of the entire class.

4. A pupil was assigned a project to conduct a sample survey to investigate the proportion of people living in the area who watched the television soap *Coronation Street*. The pupil's sample consisted of pupils from the school. Comment.

1.2   Simple Random Sampling

As mentioned above, a simple random sampling procedure is one which ensures that every possible sample of the specified size has the same chance of being the selected sample. The selected sample is then referred to as a **simple random sample** from the population. Note that the term 'random' relates to the sampling procedure and not to the actual sample. Here we shall consider a random sampling procedure when the population is finite and the items in the population are available on a numbered list.

Example 1

Obtain a simple random sample of 6 pupils from a total of 22 pupils whose names appear on a numbered list.

METHOD 1

Arrange to have a pack of 22 cards numbered from 1 to 22. Shuffle the pack well and then deal out 6 cards. The numbers on the dealt cards are then the numbers of the pupils to include in the sample.

This method will clearly become much more cumbersome if the population is a large one. A more practical method is one based on the use of **random digits**, which are a sequence of the ten digits 0, 1, 2, …, 9 in which each recorded digit is equally likely to be any one of the ten digits. Tables of random digits are readily available; in particular Table 15 in RND tables and Table 24 in the Murdoch and Barnes tables. Most calculators will have a key (probably labelled RAN) which gives random digits when pressed successively.

The following table gives 500 random digits arranged in 25 rows and 20 columns. We demonstrate the use of this table to obtain a random sample as specified in Example 1.

Row No.	Column No.																			
	1	2	3	4	5	6	7	8	9	10	11	12	13	14	15	16	17	18	19	20
1	5	9	9	6	0	1	3	6	8	8	7	7	9	0	4	5	5	9	6	4
2	7	2	0	8	5	9	4	4	6	7	9	8	5	6	6	5	1	4	9	6
3	1	0	9	1	4	6	9	6	8	6	1	9	8	3	5	2	4	7	5	3
4	6	5	0	0	5	1	9	3	5	1	3	0	8	0	0	5	1	9	2	9
5	5	6	2	3	2	7	1	9	0	3	7	3	5	2	9	3	7	0	5	0
6	4	8	2	1	4	7	7	4	6	3	1	7	2	7	2	7	5	1	2	6
7	3	5	9	6	2	9	0	0	4	5	8	4	9	0	9	0	6	5	7	7
8	6	3	9	9	2	5	6	9	0	2	0	9	0	4	0	3	3	5	7	8
9	1	9	7	9	9	5	0	7	2	1	0	2	8	4	4	8	5	1	9	7
10	2	8	5	5	5	3	0	9	4	8	8	6	2	8	3	0	0	2	3	5
11	7	1	3	0	3	2	0	6	4	7	9	3	7	4	2	1	8	6	3	3
12	4	1	9	4	5	4	0	6	5	7	4	8	2	8	0	1	8	3	8	4
13	0	9	1	1	②	1	9	1	7	3	9	7	2	8	4	4	7	4	0	6
14	2	2	3	0	9	5	6	9	7	2	3	8	5	8	2	2	1	4	7	9
15	2	4	3	2	1	2	3	8	4	2	3	3	5	6	9	0	9	2	5	7
16	8	9	1	7	9	5	8	8	2	9	0	2	3	9	5	6	0	3	4	6
17	9	7	7	4	0	6	5	6	1	7	1	4	2	3	9	8	6	1	6	7
18	7	0	5	2	8	5	0	1	5	0	0	1	8	4	0	2	7	8	4	3
19	1	0	6	2	9	8	1	9	4	1	1	8	8	3	9	9	4	7	9	9
20	4	6	4	0	6	6	4	4	5	2	9	1	3	6	7	4	4	3	5	3
21	3	0	8	2	1	3	5	4	0	0	7	8	4	5	6	3	9	8	3	5
22	5	5	0	3	3	6	6	7	6	8	4	9	0	8	9	6	2	1	4	4
23	2	5	2	7	9	9	4	1	2	8	0	7	4	1	0	8	3	4	6	6
24	1	9	4	2	7	4	3	9	9	1	4	1	9	6	5	3	7	8	7	2
25	3	7	5	6	0	8	1	8	0	9	7	7	5	3	8	4	4	6	4	7

METHOD 2

To use the table we have to arbitrarily decide on a starting point in the table and the direction of movement from that point to generate successive digits. For the starting point, close your eyes and place a finger onto the table; the starting digit is then the one nearest your fingertip. For convenience we shall always move to the right from the starting point and row by row.

Suppose that our starting point is the digit 2 in Row 13 and Column 5 (ringed in the table). Since the population size (22) has two digits we will need to take the digits in successive pairs to generate the numbers of our sample. Note that this means that any pair larger than 22 will have to be discarded and so will any pair which occurs more than once. Moving as stated above the successive pairs of digits are as follows, where the acceptable pairs are given in bold.

> **21**, 91, 73, 97, 28, 44, 74, **06** (Row 13 entries)
>
> **22**, 30, 95, 69, 72, 38, 58, 22, **14**, 79 (Row 14 entries)
>
> 24, 32, **12**, 38, 42, 33, 56, 90, 92, 57 (Row 15 entries)
>
> 89, **17**

at which point we can stop since we have generated 6 different numbers. Thus, our simple random sample will consist of those pupils numbered on the list as

6, 12, 14, 17, 21, 22.

It may be shown (using a method given in Chapter 3) that there are 74613 possible samples of size 6 from a population of size 22. The above method is such that every one of these possibilities has the same chance of being the chosen sample.

There is a chance, though unlikely, that the chosen sample will be unrepresentative of the population (e.g. ending up with the 6 tallest pupils when the variable of interest is height). If we should be unfortunate enough to end up with an unrepresentative sample, at least we can take comfort from the fact that this occurred by chance rather than by design.

The frustrating part of the above method is that we had to generate 30 pairs of digits in order to get 6 different ones. This was mainly because we had to discard every pair of digits greater than 22. We can do better than this using the following method.

METHOD 3   **The Remainder Method**

Here we shall allocate more than just one pair of digits in the range 00-99 to each listed number. To ensure parity, the allocation must be such that the same number of pairs is allocated to each listed number. Since $\frac{100}{22} = 4$ with remainder 12, we can actually allocate four pairs of digits to each listed number. It is convenient to do so by restricting the allocation to 00-87, taking 00 to correspond to the listed number 22 and discarding every pair from 88 to 99. The following shows an allocation that is simple to understand.

Pupil Number	Pairs of digits
1	01, 23, 45, 67
2	02, 24, 46, 68
3	03, 25, 47, 69
.	.
.	.
.	.
21	21, 43, 65, 87
22	00, 22, 44, 66

Note that the first pair of digits in each row other than the last is the pupil's listed number, that in the last row being 00. The other pairs of digits in a row are obtained by adding 22 successively until four pairs have been obtained. Alternatively, the pairs of digits in any row have the property that when divided by 22 (the population size) the remainder is the same. For example, dividing each of the four pairs of digits corresponding to pupil number 1, the remainder in each case is seen to be 1. For this reason this method is referred to as the **remainder method**.

Applying this method to the successive pairs of digits given in Method 2 we have

Pair of digits: 21, 91, 73, 97, 28, 44, 74, 06, 22, 30, 95, 69

Remainder: **21**, D, **7**, D, **6**, **0**, **8**, 6, 0, 8, D, **3**

where D denotes a discarded pair because it exceeds 87 and the boldfaced numbers correspond to the numbers of the pupils that are to be chosen. Note that we also ignore any number (remainder) which is repeated (6, 0 and 8 above). Thus this method has given us the sample consisting of the pupils numbered

$$3, 6, 7, 8, 21, 22.$$

Recall that a zero remainder corresponds to the last pupil (number 22) on the list.

The required sample of 6 has been achieved from just 12 pairs of digits as compared with 30 using Method 2, a reduction of 60%.

The remainder method will always be beneficial for any two-digit population size which is much less than 100. Why is this so?

To generalise the remainder method consider a population of size n where n is a two-digit number (i.e. from 10 to 99). The procedure is then as follows:

Step 1: First calculate the integer part of $\dfrac{100}{n}$; if this is k, then when applying the procedure every pair of digits from $n \times k$ upwards is to be discarded. For example, when $n = 44$, $k = 2$, all pairs from $44 \times 2 = 88$ upwards will be discarded.

Step 2: Reading off the random digits in pairs, divide each non-discarded pair by n and record the remainder. This remainder gives the item number to be selected, noting that a remainder of 0 corresponds to the last item (nth) on the list. Continue until the number of items required in the sample has been achieved.

The method extends readily to a population of size greater than 99. For instance, consider a population of size n where n is a three-digit number (i.e from 100 to 999). The procedure now is as above but replacing 100 by 1000. This is illustrated in the following example.

Example 2

Use the remainder method to obtain a simple random sample of 8 items from a population of 180 items.

First note that because the population size is a three-digit number the random digits must be taken as triples.

Step 1: The integer part of $\dfrac{1000}{180}$ is 5 so that 5 triples can be allocated to each of the 180 numbered items. We shall discard any triple from $180 \times 5 = 900$ upwards.

Step 2: Divide each triple of digits from 000 to 899 by 180 and record the remainder. The remainder is the numbered item to be selected, except that a remainder of 0 corresponds to the last numbered item (i.e. the 180th).

Using the same starting point and direction of movement as we did earlier, the triples of digits and the remainders on dividing by 180 are as follows:

Triple of digits   219 173 972 844 740 622 309 569 723

Remainder   **39 173** D **124** **20** **82 129** **29** **3**

Thus, the 8 items to be sampled are those numbered

$$3, 20, 29, 39, 82, 124, 129, 173.$$

Exercise 1.2

In each of questions 1-5 below, apply both Method 2 and the remainder method to generate the random sample required, using the table of random digits given on page 4 and taking the starting point as that given in the question. Comment on the reduction of effort from using the remainder method.

1. Obtain a random sample of 8 items from a population of 30 items, taking your starting point to be the digit in Row 13 and Column 5.

2. Obtain a random sample of 10 items from a population of 80 items, taking your starting point to be the digit in Row 5 and Column 2.

3. Obtain a random sample of 5 items from a population of 145 items, taking your starting point to be the digit in Row 2 and Column 15.

4. Obtain a random sample of 6 items from a population of 162 items, taking your starting point to be the digit in Row 1 and Column 1.

5. Obtain a random sample of 10 items from a population of 3428 items, taking your starting point to be the digit in Row 4 and Column 2. [In this case you will need to record the digits as quadruples because the population size is a four-digit number].

1.3   Stratified Sampling

Suppose a sample survey is to be carried out to investigate the sporting activities of the pupils in a co-educational school. Taking a random sample of pupils from the school could result in the chosen pupils being predominantly boys or predominantly girls. The sporting activities of boys and girls are likely to be different (more boys than girls play rugby while more girls than boys play netball). If our sample turns out to be predominantly boys or predominantly girls it is clear that the sample will not give a true picture of the sporting activities of all the pupils in the school. This suggests that our sampling method should ensure that we have a reasonable number of boys and a reasonable number of girls in our sample. Such a sample is referred to as a **stratified sample**. This may be achieved by subdividing the population into two groups, one being the boys and the other the girls. These groups are referred to as the **strata**. The procedure then is to randomly sample from each of the two groups.

Stratifying is always recommended whenever it is known that a population of items can be subdivided into two (or more) groups where it is anticipated that the responses obtained from one group are likely to be very different to those from another group.

Thus, strata are chosen because it is expected that responses within a stratum are more similar than responses from different strata.

Having identified the strata and decided on a total sample size it is then necessary to specify the size of sample to take from each stratum. If all we know are the strata sizes (i.e. the numbers of items in the strata), then a **proportional allocation** is appropriate. This means that the strata sample sizes are directly proportional to the sizes of the strata.

An important advantage of stratified random sampling as compared with random sampling the entire population is that it is more likely to give a sample which is representative of the population. It also enables the investigator to make comparisons of the responses from the strata.

The following examples illustrate the application of proportional allocation in stratified random sampling.

Example 1

A sample survey is to be conducted to investigate the reading habits of the pupils in a co-educational school. Since the reading habits of girls and boys are likely to be different it is decided to take a stratified random sample. Given that the total number of boys in the school is 270 and the total number of girls is 580, determine the proportional allocation of the sample sizes to take if the total sample size is to be 100.

The total number of pupils is 270 + 580 = 850. The proportional allocation is therefore as follows:

Number of boys to be sampled = $\frac{270}{850} \times 100 = 31.8$

Number of girls to be sampled = $\frac{580}{850} \times 100 = 68.2$.

Rounding the above figures the sample should consist of 32 boys and 68 girls.

Example 2

A company has three factories A, B and C located in different parts of the country. The company intends to conduct a sample survey on the travelling distances of the employees. Recognising that the distances may differ from one factory to another because of their locations it is decided to conduct stratified sampling. Given that the numbers of employees in the three factories are 1200, 2000 and 3600, respectively, and that the total sample size is to be 200, determine the sizes of the samples that should be taken from the three factories.

The total number of employees is $1200 + 2000 + 3600 = 6800$.

The allocations of sample sizes are:

$$\text{Factory A:} \quad \frac{1200}{6800} \times 200 = 35.3,$$
$$\text{Factory B:} \quad \frac{2000}{6800} \times 200 = 58.8,$$
$$\text{Factory C:} \quad \frac{3600}{6800} \times 200 = 105.9.$$

Rounding the calculated figures, the sample sizes should be 35, 59 and 106, respectively.

Exercise 1.3

1. A sample survey is to be conducted to investigate the weekly amount of pocket money received by the boys in Years 12 and 13. It is decided to take a stratified sample of total size 24 with proportional allocation. There are 35 boys in Year 12 and 25 in Year 13.

    (a) Determine the sample sizes.

    (b) Assuming that there are numbered lists of the boys in the two years, use the remainder method to determine which boys should be selected from Year 12. Use the table of random digits given on page 4 and start from the top left of the table (Row 1, Column 1) and move right and from one row to the next.

2. In a sample survey on the wages and salaries paid to employees at a large factory suggest a variable for which stratified sampling should be used.

3. A sample survey is to be conducted to investigate the attitudes of pupils at a school towards scenes of violence shown on television. It is thought that the pupils' attitudes may vary with age, so it is decided to stratify the school population according to the age-groups 11-13, 14-16, and 17+. The numbers of pupils in the school in these age groups are 352, 284 and 103, respectively. If the total sample size is to be 120, find the sizes of the random samples to be taken from the three age-groups. Use the remainder method to determine the numbers of the pupils in the age-group 17+ that should be sampled.

1.4   Cluster Sampling

It may happen that a population divides naturally into different groups with a listing of the items in each group. For example, the pupils of a school are in forms and the voters in a general election are in the various constituencies. Such groups are referred to as **clusters**. In such a situation it may well be more convenient administratively and more cost-effective in a sample survey to initially select a random sample of clusters. One may then include every item in a sampled cluster or take a random sample of items from each cluster.

There is an essential difference between strata and clusters. In the former, one expects responses from within a stratum to be more alike than responses from different strata, but in the latter it is likely that responses within a cluster will be similar for all the clusters.

Suppose that the National Assembly wants to conduct a sample survey to obtain information on all the primary school pupils in Wales. Taking a random sample of all the pupils would be a major task. The primary schools are administered by the various local education authorities, which are natural clusters. So a good procedure would be to first randomly select some local education authorities (the precise number to be determined from other considerations). The next step would be to obtain a list of all the primary schools in each area; if there are many of these it may be necessary to select a random sample from each list. Finally the survey may include all the pupils in each sampled primary school or may take random samples of pupils from each selected school. This clearly indicates that cluster sampling is a technique which is aimed at administrative convenience.

Exercise 1.4

1.   State briefly the difference between stratified sampling and cluster sampling. Give one example of each technique.

2.   A sample survey is to be carried out on some characteristics of the population of boys in a school. Suggest how the population may be subdivided into clusters. State the advantage here of using cluster sampling as compared with complete random sampling.

Chapter 2

Descriptive Statistics

2.1 Introduction

Descriptive Statistics is concerned with meaningful and informative representations of a set of data (observed values of a variable). Such a representation may be in the form of a table, a diagram, or summary measures to quantify some important characteristics of the data. You will have studied Descriptive Statistics in the Handling Data section of your GCSE course in Mathematics. In this chapter we shall be considering topics not included in the Intermediate Level of the GCSE course. It will be assumed that you are familiar with the following terms.

Discrete frequency distributions and vertical diagrams,

Mode, median and mean; range and interquartile range,

Grouped frequency distributions and diagrams (equal interval widths), including cumulative frequency diagrams.

The topics to be covered in this chapter include:

The mean and standard deviation of a set of data (ungrouped and grouped),

Histogram and cumulative frequency representations of a grouped frequency distribution when the class intervals are not all of the same width.

Exercise 2.1 (Revision)

1. The keyboard speeds, in words per minute, of eleven secretaries were:

    36, 40, 51, 42, 43, 40, 46, 45, 46, 39, 42 .

    Determine the mean, the median, the range and the interquartile range of these speeds.

2. The number of children per family in 40 families had the following frequency distribution.

Number of children per family	1	2	3	4	5
Number of families	11	10	8	7	4

    Determine the mean, the median, the range and the interquartile range of this distribution.

3. The following table shows a grouped frequency distribution of the heights, measured correct to the nearest centimetre, of 30 boys.

Measured height (cm) 158-160 161-163 164-166 167-169 170-172 173-175

Number of boys   1   4   10   8   5   2

(a) Display the distribution as a grouped frequency diagram.

(b) Construct a cumulative frequency diagram for the distribution. Use your diagram to estimate (i) the median, (ii) the interquartile range of the heights.

(c) Calculate an estimate of the mean height of the 30 boys.

2.2   Mean and standard deviation of a set of ungrouped data

Two characteristics of a set of data that merit summary measures are:

(1) a value that is representative of the observations, which is referred to as a **measure of location** (or of central tendency),

(2) a value which indicates the variation of the observations in the set of data, which is referred to as a **measure of spread** (or dispersion).

Measures of location that you are assumed to be familiar with are:

the mode, the median and the mean.

Measures of spread that you are assumed to be familiar with are:

the range and the interquartile range.

In this chapter we shall introduce the most widely used measure of spread known as the **standard deviation**.

The mean of a set of data is defined to be

The sum of the observations in the set of data

The number of observations in the set of data

Denoting the observed variable by x, the mean is generally denoted by $\bar{x}$ (pronounced 'x bar'). Thus if there are *n* observations having the values x_1, x_2, ..., x_n, the sum of the observations is

$$x_1 + x_2 + \ldots + x_n \equiv \sum_{i=1}^{n} x_i$$

where Σ is the capital Greek letter 'sigma' and is used here to denote 'sum of'. In this notation the mean is

$$\bar{x} = \frac{\sum_{i=1}^{n} x_i}{n} \, .$$

Example 1

A householder's weekly consumption of electricity, in kilowatt-hours (kWh), during a period of 5 weeks were: 338, 354, 341, 353, 351. Calculate the mean weekly consumption of electricity.

Solution

The sum of the observations is $\Sigma x = 338 + 354 + 341 + 353 + 351 = 1737$
and the mean consumption is

$$\bar{x} = \frac{1737}{5} = 347.4 \text{ kWh}$$

Standard deviation

With $\bar{x}$ as our measure of location it makes sense to have a measure of spread dependent on the deviations of the individual observations from $\bar{x}$ (namely $x_i - \bar{x}$). The deviations in our example are:

$$(338 - 347.4), (354 - 347.4), (341 - 347.4), (353 - 347.4), (351 - 347.4)$$
$$= -9.4, +6.6, -6.4, +5.6, +3.6.$$

Now consider combining these in some way to give a numerical value for the measure of spread. As is true for any set of data, these deviations sum to zero, so taking their average (mean) as the measure of spread is not appropriate. Instead, consider taking the average of the squares of the deviations as the measure of spread, which is called the **variance** of the set of data and will be denoted by Var. For the above example, the mean of the squared deviations is

$$\text{Var} = \left[\frac{(-9.4)^2 + (6.6)^2 + (-6.4)^2 + (5.6)^2 + (3.6)^2}{5} \right] = 43.44 \text{ kWh}^2.$$

Observe that the units of Var will always be the square of the variable units (kWh^2 here). For a measure of spread having the same units as the variable we take the square root of Var, which is called the **standard deviation** of the set of data and will be denoted by SD. For the above example the standard deviation is

$$\text{SD} = \sqrt{43.44} = 6.591 \text{ kWh (correct to three decimal places).}$$

To generalise the above, consider the n observations $x_1, x_2, \ldots, x_n$, having mean $\bar{x}$. The sum of the squares of the deviations from $\bar{x}$ is

$$(x_1 - \bar{x})^2 + (x_2 - \bar{x})^2 + \ldots (x_n - \bar{x})^2 \equiv \sum_{i=1}^{n} (x_i - \bar{x})^2,$$

so that the variance is

$$\text{Var} = \frac{\sum_{i=1}^{n} (x_i - \bar{x})^2}{n} \qquad (1)$$

and the standard deviation is $SD = \sqrt{Var}$.

The arithmetic involved in finding SD can be simplified on using the identity

$$\sum_{i=1}^{n}(x_i - \overline{x})^2 = \sum_{i=1}^{n}x_i^2 - \frac{\left(\sum_{i=1}^{n}x_i\right)^2}{n} \qquad (2)$$

the derivation of which is left as an exercise. Using (2), the calculation of the standard deviation of the data in Example 1 can be set out in a table as follows.

	x	x^2
	338	114244
	354	125316
	341	116281
	353	124609
	351	123201
Total	1737	603651

Thus, $\Sigma x = 1737$ and $\Sigma x^2 = 603651$. Substituting in (2) and using (1) we have

$$Var = \frac{1}{5}\left(603651 - \frac{1737^2}{5}\right) = 43.44$$

and $SD = \sqrt{43.44} = 6.591$ correct to three decimal places, as obtained earlier.

If your calculator has a Statistics (or SD) mode then the calculation is simpler still. You will need to check the manual of your calculator for the procedure to follow. Many calculators with this mode will have a key labelled $\overline{x}$ (for the mean) and two keys labelled s_n and s_{n-1} or σ_n and σ_{n-1}, the one with subscript n being the one to use for the standard deviation as defined here.

Exercise 2.2

In Questions 1 to 6 calculate the mean and the standard deviation of each set of data, giving your answers correct to three decimal places.

1.   The numbers of days that 5 pupils had been absent from school during a school year were: 4, 3, 8, 6, 4, respectively.

2. The heights, in cm, of 7 boys were : 159, 167, 170, 170, 174, 173, 162.

3. The lengths, in mm, of 10 cuckoo eggs were:

    18, 21, 19, 20, 18, 18, 19, 21, 20, 18.

4. The percentage marks scored by a pupil in 8 subjects were:

    36, 49, 62, 74, 25, 39, 53, 62.

5. The keyboard speeds, in words per minute, of 10 clerks working in a large office were:

    37, 45, 41, 37, 39, 41, 41, 38, 43, 40.

6. The times, in seconds, gained (plus values) or lost (minus values) by 10 watches over a period of 24 hours were:

    +1.1, +4.2, −2.3, +3.4, +0.7, −4.1, +3.9, −3.0, +3.1, +1.0

7. The playing times, in minutes, of five C60 cassettes of make A were:

    42.3, 42.1, 53.2, 48.6, 51.8,

    and of five C60 cassettes of make B were:

    44.1, 46.5, 50.1, 48.2, 52.1.

    (a) Which make had the longer mean playing time?

    (b) Which make had the more variable playing time?

    (c) State, giving a reason for your choice, which make you would recommend to buy.

8. A set of 10 observed values of a variable x were such that

    $$\Sigma x = 290 \quad \text{and} \quad \Sigma x^2 = 8469.$$

    Calculate the mean and the variance of the data.

9. In 5 successive cricket innings a batsman's scores were: 11, 58, 36, 0, 41.

    (a) Determine how many runs this batsman must score in his next innings to give him a mean score of 30 over the 6 innings.

    (b) Assuming that the batsman's mean score for the 6 innings is equal to 30, calculate the standard deviation of the 6 scores, giving your answer correct to three decimal places.

10. The 5 numbers 5, 7, 8, a, b have mean 6 and variance 2. Given that b is greater than a, find the values of a and b.

2.3   Mean and standard deviation of a discrete frequency distribution

Example

The following table shows the frequency distribution of the number of matches per box in 50 boxes of matches. Calculate the mean and the standard deviation of the number of matches per box.

Number of matches in box (x)	43	44	45	46	47	48
Number of boxes (frequency f)	3	8	14	16	8	1

Solution

Since 3 of the boxes contained 43 matches, 8 contained 44 matches, et cetera, the total number of matches in the 50 boxes is

$$\Sigma x = 3 \times 43 + 8 \times 44 + 14 \times 45 + 16 \times 46 + 8 \times 47 + 1 \times 48 = 2271.$$

Hence, the mean number of matches per box is $\bar{x} = \dfrac{2271}{50} = 45.42$.

Similarly the sum of the squares of the numbers of matches in the boxes is

$$\Sigma x^2 = 3 \times 43^2 + 8 \times 44^2 + 14 \times 45^2 + 16 \times 46^2 + 8 \times 47^2 + 1 \times 48^2 = 103217.$$

Using (2) of Section 2.2 we have

$$\Sigma(x - \bar{x})^2 = 103217 - \left(\frac{2271^2}{50} \right) = 68.18.$$

It follows that the variance of the distribution is

$$\text{Var} = \frac{68.18}{50} = 1.3636$$

and the standard deviation is SD $= \sqrt{1.3636} = 1.168$ correct to three decimal places.

To generalise, consider a data set of n observations having the **distinct** values $x_1, x_2, ..., x_r$ occurring with frequencies $f_1, f_2, ... f_r$, respectively, as shown in the following table.

Variable value	x_1	x_2	x_3	...	x_r
Frequency	f_1	f_2	f_3	...	f_r

The mean of this distribution is

$$\bar{x} = \frac{(f_1 x_1 + f_2 x_2 + f_3 x_3 + ... f_r x_r)}{n} = \frac{\sum_{i=1}^{r} f_i x_i}{n},$$

where $n = f_1 + f_2 + f_3 + ... + f_r = \sum_{i=1}^{r} f_i$ is the total frequency.

The sum of the squares of all n observations is

$$f_1 x_1^2 + f_2 x_2^2 + f_3 x_3^2 + ... + f_r x_r^2 = \sum_{i=1}^{r} f_i x_i^2$$

The variance is

$$VAR = \frac{1}{n}\left[\sum_{i=1}^{r}f_i x_i^2 - \frac{\left(\sum_{i=1}^{r}f_i x_i\right)^2}{n}\right]$$

These expressions provide a convenient tabular method for finding the mean and standard deviation of a given frequency distribution, as illustrated below for our example.

x	f	fx	fx^2
43	3	129	5547
44	8	352	15488
45	14	630	28350
46	16	736	33856
47	8	376	17672
48	1	48	2304
Total	50	2271	103217

[Note well that the final column headed $fx^2 = f \times x^2 = f \times x \times x$]
From the final row of the table we have

$$n = 50, \ \Sigma fx = 2271, \ \Sigma fx^2 = 103217$$

as obtained earlier.

[Some calculators will have a pre-programmed facility for finding the mean and the standard deviation of a discrete frequency distribution. Check to see if your calculator has a key labelled f; if so refer to the manual for procedural instructions.]

Exercise 2.3

Calculate the mean and the standard deviation, correct to three decimal places, of each of the following frequency distributions.

1. The table shows the frequency distribution of the number of children per family in 30 families.

Number of children	0	1	2	3	4
Number of families	6	9	11	3	1

2. The scores obtained in 50 throws of a cubical die are shown in the following table.

Score	1	2	3	4	5	6
Frequency	8	12	15	10	3	2

3. A business concern sent 40 letters by first-class mail one day and then checked when the letters were delivered. The number of days to delivery had the following distribution.

Number of days to delivery	1	2	3	4
Number of letters	14	12	10	4

4. The following table shows the distribution of the number of orders received per week by a company throughout 1999.

Number of orders	50	51	52	53	54	55	56
Number of weeks	4	6	8	10	15	7	2

5. The following table shows the frequency distribution of the number of 'bubbles' per glass bottle in a sample of 40 bottles.

Number of 'bubbles'	0	1	2	3	4
Number of bottles	15	11	10	3	1

6. The number of road accidents per day that occurred in a certain county was recorded over a period of 100 days with the following results.

Number of accidents	0	1	2	3	4	5	6	7	8
Number of days	5	15	22	23	17	10	5	2	1

7. The following table shows the frequency distribution of the shoe sizes of 36 boys.

Shoe size	$6\frac{1}{2}$	7	$7\frac{1}{2}$	8	$8\frac{1}{2}$	9
Number of boys	3	6	12	8	5	2

8. The following table shows the frequency distribution of the number of winners of the jackpot prize in 25 draws of the *National Lottery*.

Number of winners	0	1	2	4	5	8
Number of draws	2	3	8	6	4	2

2.4   Mean and standard deviation given a grouped frequency distribution

When a set of data is only available in the form of a grouped frequency distribution it is not possible to calculate the exact values of the mean and standard deviation since the individual observed values are not known. However, reasonable estimates can be obtained. The method is based on the assumption that the observations in any class interval were distributed evenly over the interval, in which case one is justified in replacing each class interval by its midpoint value. This is justified in the sense that the product of the interval midpoint and frequency will be equal to the sum of the observations in the interval. Thus, the problem is reduced to a frequency distribution and the method of the preceding section can be used to determine estimates of the mean and standard deviation. This is illustrated in the following examples of grouped frequency distributions whose class intervals are not all of the same width.

Example 1

The following table shows a grouped frequency distribution of the last-birthday ages, in years, of the 55 people killed in road accidents in a certain county.

Age (years)	0-19	20-29	30-49	50-79	80-99
Frequency	13	23	11	5	3

Estimate, to the nearest month, the mean and the standard deviation of the ages.

Solution

The first step in the solution is to replace each class interval (age-group) by its midpoint value. Since ages are recorded in years at a person's last birthday, the interval 0-19 will include every person who has not reached the age of 20 years; the midpoint of this interval is $\frac{1}{2}(0 + 20) = 10$.

Similarly, the midpoint of the interval 20-29 is $\frac{1}{2}(20 + 30) = 25$,

that of the interval 30-49 is $\frac{1}{2}(30 + 50) = 40$,

that of the interval 50-79 is $\frac{1}{2}(50 + 80) = 65$,

and that of the last interval 80-99 is $\frac{1}{2}(80 + 100) = 90$.

Replacing each class interval by its midpoint we have the following frequency distribution.

Midpoint age (x years)	10	25	40	65	90
Frequency (f)	13	23	11	5	3

Solution

It is left as an exercise, using the method of Section 2.3, to show that

the estimated mean age is $\bar{x} = 31.6364$ years $= 31$ years 8 months, and the estimated standard deviation is SD = 20.7376 years = 20 years 9 months.

Example 2

The breaking strains of 150 ropes were measured correct to the nearest kilogram, the results obtained being as shown in the following table. Estimate, correct to the nearest kilogram, the mean and the standard deviation of the breaking strains.

Breaking strain (kg)	100-149	150-299	300-499	500-599	600-699
Number of ropes	16	33	50	41	10

Solution

In this example the measurements have been recorded to the nearest kilogram. Thus, for example, the class interval 100-149 includes all the ropes with a breaking strain ranging from 99.5 kg to 149.5 kg, so that the midpoint is $\frac{1}{2}(99.5 + 149.5) = 124.5$.

Note that this value is also the mean of the endpoints of the class interval 100-149, which provides a simpler method for obtaining the midpoints in this example. Treating the other class intervals similarly, the frequency distribution of the interval midpoints is as follows:

Midpoint value (kg)	124.5	224.5	399.5	549.5	649.5
Frequency	16	33	50	41	10

It is again left as an exercise to use the method of Section 2.3 to show that the estimated mean and standard deviation of the breaking strains are 389 kg and 158 kg, respectively, correct to the nearest kilogram.

Exercise 2.4

Obtain estimates of the mean and the standard deviation given each of the following grouped frequency distributions.

1. The following table shows a grouped frequency distribution compiled from the ages, in years, of 50 males when they got married.

Age at marriage (years)	16-21	22-27	28-33	34-39	40-45	46-63
Number of males	7	14	12	8	4	5

2. The cephalic index (a measure of head shape) of each of 100 pupils was measured to the nearest whole number with the following results.

Cephalic Index	69-	75-	77-	79-	81-	83-	87-91
Number of pupils	4	12	26	28	19	9	2

3. The following table shows a grouped frequency table of the distances driven, in thousands of kilometres, by 100 car drivers in a particular year.

Distance (x thousand km)	Number of drivers
$2 \leq x < 10$	6
$10 \leq x < 26$	34
$26 \leq x < 34$	36
$34 \leq x < 42$	15
$42 \leq x < 50$	9

4. The masses, measured to the nearest gram, of 150 oranges had the following grouped frequency distribution.

Mass (g)	100-139	140-179	180-199	200-219	220-239	240-279	280-320
No. of oranges	8	15	24	41	45	12	5

5. The masses, to the nearest kilogram, of the parcels mailed in one day at a post office had the following grouped frequency distribution.

Mass (kg)	1	2	3-4	5-6	7-9	10-15
Number of parcels	3	5	12	18	21	24

6. The age distributions of 100 residents on a housing estate in a town and 200 residents on a housing estate in a seaside resort are shown in the following table.

Age (years)	0-14	15-29	30-44	45-59	60-74	75-89
No. in town	12	22	30	19	12	5
No. in resort	4	24	42	52	62	16

From your values for the means and standard deviations, comment on the main differences between the two distributions and suggest a reason for the differences.

2.5 Histograms

A **histogram** is a diagram which is appropriate for displaying a grouped frequency distribution, especially when the class intervals are not all of the same width. The following examples illustrate the method for constructing a histogram given a grouped frequency distribution.

Example 1

The following table shows a grouped frequency distribution of the ages of 100 persons living on a housing estate.

Age (years)	0-4	5-14	15-29	30-44	45-59	60-79	80-99
Frequency	6	16	21	20	18	13	6

Display the distribution diagrammatically.

Solution

Suppose that we decided to display the distribution in the form of a grouped frequency diagram by erecting a rectangle above each class interval with height equal to the corresponding frequency. The resulting diagram is shown in Figure 1a.

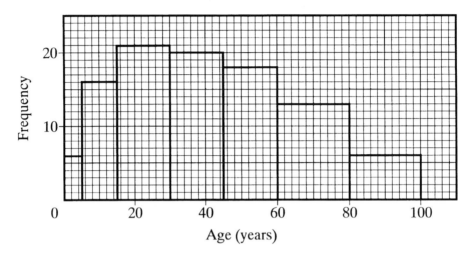

Figure 1(a)

Now compare the first and last rectangles. They have the same height (frequency 6) but the width of the last rectangle (20 years) is four times the width of the first rectangle (5 years). Thus, area-wise, the last rectangle is four times the first rectangle. Since the size of a rectangle is visually seen as its area, the above diagram would imply that there are four times as many persons aged 80-99 as aged 0-4, whereas, in fact, there are 6 persons in each age-group. For an appropriate diagram it is clear that when the interval widths are not all equal the widths have to be taken into account when representing the distribution diagrammatically. This may be done by using **frequency densities** instead of frequencies, where

$$\text{the frequency density of an interval} = \frac{\text{Frequency of the interval}}{\text{Width of the interval}},$$

which is simply the frequency per unit variable. The procedure is illustrated for Example 1 in the following table and the resulting diagram (Figure 1b) which is called a **histogram**.

Age (years)	0-4	5-14	15-29	30-44	45-59	60-79	80-99
Interval width (w)	5	10	15	15	15	20	20
Frequency (f)	6	16	21	20	18	13	6
Frequency density (f/w)	1.2	1.6	1.4	1.33	1.2	0.65	0.3

The essential property of a histogram is that the "area" of the rectangle above a class interval (obtained by multiplying the interval width by the frequency density) is numerically equal to the frequency of that interval. Thus, comparing "areas" of the rectangles is equivalent to comparing frequencies. In particular, the total "area" under the histogram is numerically equal to the total frequency (the number of observations in the given set of data).

For a grouped frequency distribution having unequal interval widths, the interval having the highest frequency density is called the **modal class.** In the above example the age-group having the highest frequency is 15-29 but the modal class is 5-14, being the interval with the highest frequency density.

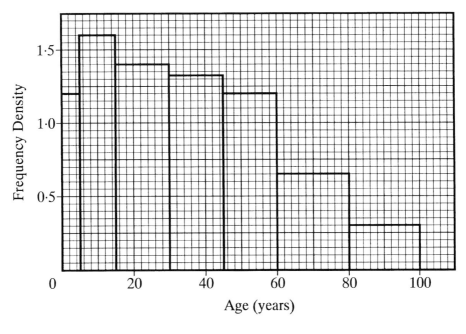

Figure 1(b)

Example 2

The masses of 80 athletes were measured to the nearest kilogram, and the following grouped frequency distribution was constructed from the results. Display the distribution as a histogram

Mass (kg)	75-82	83-84	85-86	87-88	89-93	94-98
Frequency	10	5	10	11	34	10

Solution

Since the masses were measured to the nearest kilogram, the interval 75-82 includes every athlete having a mass between 74.5 kg and 82.5 kg, which are often referred to as the **class boundaries** of the interval 75-82. The other intervals are interpreted similarly. The following table shows the calculation of the frequency densities.

Mass (kg)	74.5-82.5	82.5-84.5	84.5-86.5	86.5-88.5	88.5-93.5	93.5-98.5
Width (w)	8	2	2	2	5	5
Frequency (f)	10	5	10	11	34	10
Freq. density (f/w)	1.25	2.5	5	5.5	6.8	2

The histogram is shown in *Figure 2*.

It so happens in this example that that the modal class interval (89-93) is also the one with the highest frequency, but this is not always the case as we saw in Example 1.

Recall that the median of a set of data is the value of the middle observation when the observations are ordered in magnitude. Since here we do not have the values of the individual observations the best we can do is to estimate the median. The estimate is that variable value such that the "area" under the histogram to the left (or right) of it is one half of the total "area" under the histogram. Similarly, the lower quartile is that variable value such that the "area" under the histogram to the left of it is equal to one quarter of the total "area" under the histogram, and the upper quartile is that variable value such that the "area" under the histogram to its left is three-quarters of the total "area" under the histogram. Determining these values from a histogram is tedious. We describe a much simpler method in the next section.

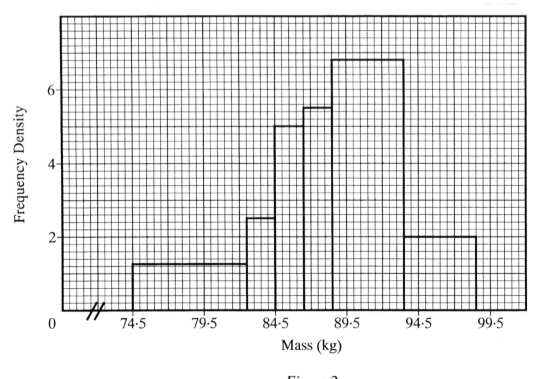

Figure 2

The shapes of the histograms in *Figure 1b* and *Figure 2* are very different. In *Figure 1b* the "tail" to the right of the modal class is longer than the "tail" to the left. Such a distribution is said to be **positively skewed** (or skewed to the right). In *Figure 2* the "tail" to the left of the modal class is longer than the "tail" to the right; such a distribution is said to be **negatively skewed** (or skewed to the left). When the "tails" on both sides are equivalent the distribution is said to be **symmetrical.** For a symmetrical distribution, the mean and the median will be equal. For a positively skewed distribution, the mean will be greater than the median, since the relatively large values are taken into account when estimating the mean but they do not affect the median. Similarly, for a negatively skewed distribution the mean will be less than the median.

Exercise 2.5

1-5   For each of the grouped frequency distributions in Questions 1-5 of Exercise 2.4

  (a) display the distribution as a histogram,

  (b) state the shape of the distribution,

  (c) write down the modal class interval,

  (d) state whether the mean is greater than, less than or approximately equal to the median.

2.6   Cumulative frequency distribution

Recall that the cumulative frequency of any value in a set of data is the number of observations in the set less than or equal to that value. Given only a grouped frequency distribution of the observations, it is not possible to determine the cumulative frequency of every value that was observed. In fact, we can only determine the cumulative frequencies of the upper class boundaries. Plotting the cumulative frequencies against the corresponding upper class boundaries and joining the plotted points by straight lines provides us with another diagrammatic representation of a grouped frequency distribution, which is known as the **cumulative frequency polygon.** The straight line joins of the plotted points is justified if the observations in any class interval are uniformly distributed over that interval (precisely the assumption we made when estimating the mean and the standard deviation from a grouped frequency distribution).

The cumulative frequency polygon provides a simple means for estimating the median and quartiles. If the total number of observations is n, then the median can be obtained from the cumulative frequency polygon by reading off the variable value when the cumulative frequency is equal to $\frac{1}{2}$n (even when this is not an integer). Similarly, the quartiles can be estimated by reading off the variable values when the cumulative frequency has the values $\frac{1}{4}$n and $\frac{3}{4}$ n, respectively. The procedure is illustrated in the examples that follow. The values can also be calculated using linear interpolation within the class interval that includes the quantity being estimated. The procedures described above are demonstrated in the example given below. The quartiles of a set of data are three variable values that subdivide the ordered observations into four parts. This idea can be extended. For example, the **deciles** are nine variable values that divide the ordered observations into 10 parts, with one-tenth of the observations being less than the lowest (first) decile, one-tenth being greater than the highest (last) decile, and one-tenth between any two successive deciles. Extending the idea further, the **percentiles** are the variable values that divide the ordered observations into 100 parts, 1% of the observations having values between any two successive percentiles. Just as the interquartile range can be used as a measure of spread so can appropriately chosen interpercentile ranges be used as measures of spread. A frequently used interpercentile range as a measure of spread is the 10-90 one, being the 90th percentile minus the 10th percentile. Observe that the median is the 50th percentile, the lower quartile is the 25th percentile and the upper quartile is the 75th percentile, so that the interquartile range is the 25-75 interpercentile range.

Example

Estimate the median, the interquartile range, and the 10-90 interpercentile range given the grouped frequency distribution in Example 2 of the preceding section.

Solution

The table of upper class boundaries and cumulative frequencies are as follows.

Mass (kg)	74.5	82.5	84.5	86.5	88.5	93.5	98.5
Cumulative frequency (CF)	0	10	15	25	36	70	80

Note that the first pair of entries has been included since we know that there was no athlete having a mass less than 74.5 kg. The cumulative frequency polygon is shown in *Figure 3*. Note that it is advisable to have easy to read scales along both axes since readings are to be taken from the graph.

Since the total number of observations is n = 80, the median m is the mass for which

$CF = \dfrac{80}{2} = 40$, which from the graph is seen to be 89 kg.

The lower quartile LQ is the mass for which $CF = \dfrac{80}{4} = 20$, and from the graph we see that LQ = 85.5kg. The upper quartile UQ is the mass for which $CF = \frac{3}{4} \times 80 = 60$.

From the graph, UQ = 92 kg. Thus, the interquartile range IQR is 92 − 85.5 = 6.5 kg .

For the 10-90 interpercentile range we need the values of the 90th and 10th percentiles. The 90th percentile is the mass for which CF = 90% of 80 = 72, which from the graph is equal to 94.5 kg.

The 10th percentile is the mass for which CF = 10% of 80 = 8, which from the graph is equal to 81 kg.

The 10-90 interpercentile range is 94.5 – 81 = 13.5 kg.

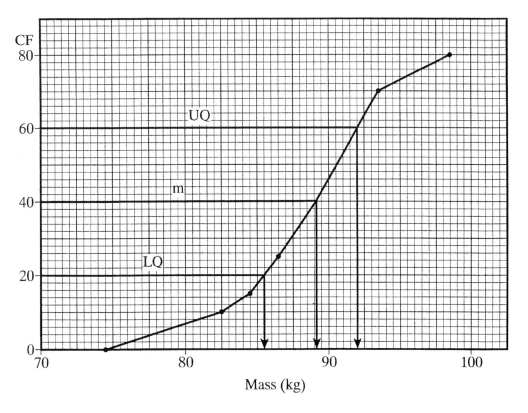

Figure 3

Alternatively, the above estimates can be calculated using linear interpolation,

which will generally give more accurate estimates.

The median is the value for which CF = 40.

From the given table we see that CF = 40 falls in the interval 88.5-93.5.

The CF for 88.5 is 36 and for 93.5 is 70. Linearly interpolating in this interval the value m for which CF = 40 is

$$m = 88.5 + \frac{40 - 36}{70 - 36} \times (93.5 - 88.5)$$

$$= 89.1 \text{ kg (to 1 dp)}.$$

The lower quartile (LQ) is the mass when CF = 20, which falls in the interval 84.5 – 86.5. The CF at the lower endpoint is 15 and at the upper endpoint is 25.

Thus, by linear interpolation, the lower quartile is given by

$$LQ = 84.5 + \frac{20 - 15}{25 - 15} \times (86.5 - 84.5) = 85.5 \text{ kg}$$

Similarly, the upper quartile is given by

$$UQ = 88.5 + \frac{60 - 36}{70 - 36} \times (93.5 - 88.5) = 92.0 \text{ kg} .$$

Thus, the interquartile range (IQR) is IQR = 92.0 – 85.5 = 6.5 kg.

Finally, the 90th percentile (CF = 90% of 80 = 72)) is estimated as

$$93.5 + \frac{72 - 70}{80 - 70} \times (98.5 - 93.5) = 94.5 \text{ kg}$$

and the 10th percentile (CF = 10% of 80 = 8) is estimated as

$$74.5 + \frac{8 - 0}{10 - 0} \times (82.5 - 74.5) = 80.9.$$

Thus, the 10-90 interpercentile range is 94.5 – 80.9 = 13.6.

Exercise 2.6

1. Estimate the median and interquartile range of the ages of 50 males given the grouped frequency distribution in Question 1 of Exercise 2.4.

2. Given the grouped frequency distribution of the cephalic indices in Question 2 of Exercise 2.4, obtain estimates, graphically or otherwise, of the median and the 10-90 interpercentile range.

3. Estimate the interquartile range of the distances travelled given in the grouped frequency distribution in Question 3 of Exercise 2.4.

4. Estimate the median and the 70th percentile of the masses of the oranges in Question 4 of Exercise 2.4.

5. Estimate the median and the interquartile range of the masses of the parcels given in Question 5 of Exercise 2.4.

6. Draw the cumulative frequency polygons for the two age distributions in Question 6 of Exercise 2.4. Use your graphs to estimate the median and the interquartile range of each distribution. Comment on the differences. [Compare with your answers to Question 6 of Exercise 2.4.]

Miscellaneous Questions on Chapter 2

1. The following table shows the frequency distribution of the number of wrong answers given by 50 people in a multiple choice test paper.

No. of wrong answers	2	3	4	5	6	7	8	9	10
No. of people	2	3	5	6	10	9	8	6	1

    Determine the mode, the median, the mean, the interquartile range and the standard deviation of the distribution.

2. An inspection for a sample of 60 books stocked in a library gave the following frequency distribution for the number of times the books had been borrowed during the preceding year.

No. of times borrowed	1	2	3	4	5
No. of books	27	16	8	5	4

    (a) Determine the median and the interquartile range of the distribution.

    (b) Calculate the mean and the standard deviation of the distribution.

3. The table shows a grouped frequency distribution of the gains in masses, measured to the nearest gram, of 30 pigs over a period of 30 days.

Mass gain (grams)	7-16	17-21	22-26	27-31	32-36	37-44
No. of pigs	4	6	9	6	3	2

    (a) Calculate estimates of the mean and the standard deviation of the gains.

    (b) Graphically, or otherwise, obtain estimates of the median and the interquartile range of the gains.

4. The yields, to the nearest tenth of a kilogram, of wheat grown in 200 fields gave the following grouped frequency distribution.

Yield (kg)	1.3-1.9	2.0-2.4	2.5-2.8	2.9-3.2	3.3-3.9
Frequency	20	42	78	36	24

    (a) Draw a histogram of the distribution.

    (b) Estimate the median and the mean yield per field. Comment on their relative values.

5. The following table shows the distribution of the ages on their last birthdays of a sample of 120 students at a university.

Age (years)	18	19	20	21	22	23
No. of students	50	32	22	8	6	2

    (a) Estimate the mean age of the students giving your answer in years and months correct to the nearest month.

    (b)   Estimate, to the nearest month in each case, the median and the 10-90 interpercentile range of the ages.

6.   A factory employs a total of 200 persons, of whom 120 have been at the factory for more than 10 years. A grouped frequency distribution of the lengths of service of the 120 persons with more than 10 years service is given in the following table.

Length of service (x years)	$10 < x \leq 15$	$15 < x \leq 20$	$20 < x \leq 25$	$25 < x \leq 30$	$30 < x \leq 40$
No. of persons	30	42	25	15	8

    (a) Draw a histogram to display this distribution.

    (b) Estimate the median and the interquartile range of the distribution.

    (c) Estimate the median length of service of all 200 employees.

    (d) Given that the mean length of service of the 80 employees with 10 years or less of service is 4.25 years, estimate the mean length of service of all 200 employees.

Chapter 3

Probability

3.1 Random Experiments

Probability, as a subject, has been developed to deal with situations in which there is uncertainty. One class of such situations is that where the uncertainty is associated with a *random experiment*, defined as follows.

Definition. A random experiment is a course of action whose outcome is not predictable and is such that repeated trials (performances) of the action may give different outcomes.

Some examples of simple random experiments are as follows;

1. Tossing a coin.
2. Throwing an ordinary cubical die.
3. Dealing two cards from an ordinary pack of playing cards.

Definition. The set of all the possible outcomes of a random experiment is called the *sample space* and will be denoted by S.

Example 1

When tossing a coin and noting the face that is uppermost, the outcome may be a head (H) or a tail (T). In this case S = {H, T}, the curly brackets indicating that the order of the elements in the brackets is irrelevant, so that we could also write S = {T, H}.

Example 2

When throwing an ordinary cubical die and noting the score that is obtained, the outcome could be any one of 1, 2, 3, 4, 5, 6. Thus,

$$S = \{1, 2, 3, 4, 5, 6\}$$

Example 3

When dealing a card from an ordinary pack of 52 playing cards and noting its suit, the outcome could be any one of Hearts, Clubs, Diamonds or Spades. In this case

$$S = \{Hearts,\ Clubs,\ Diamonds,\ Spades\}.$$

Example 4

Consider the experiment when a cubical die is thrown twice. If a note is made of the individual scores obtained, then the sample space can be written as

$$S = \{(x, y): x = 1, 2, 3, 4, 5, 6, y = 1, 2, 3, 4, 5, 6\},$$

which consists of 36 elements, each being an ordered pair of numbers, the first (x) being the score on the first throw and the second (y) the score on the second throw. If, instead, a note is to be made of the sum of the two scores obtained, then the sample space will be

$$S = \{2, 3, 4, 5, 6, 7, 8, 9, 10, 11, 12\}.$$

Exercise 3.1

Write down the appropriate sample space for each of the following random experiments.

1. A hand of 4 cards is dealt from an ordinary pack of 52 playing cards and a count is made of the number of aces in the hand.

2. A litter of six kittens is to be examined to determine how many are female.

3. A box contains 3 white balls and 1 red ball. The balls are to be drawn from the box one after another until the red ball is drawn. A note is to be made of the number of balls drawn.

4. Two balls are drawn one after the other from a bag which contains several red balls and several white balls. A record is to be made of the colours of the balls in the order in which they are drawn.

5. A coin is tossed three times. (a) A note is to be made of the outcomes of the three tosses. (b) A note is to be made of the number of heads tossed.

6. A coin is tossed until a head is obtained. A note is to be made of the number of times the coin has to be tossed

3.2 Events

Definition. An *event* is a property associated with the outcomes of a random experiment, or, in set theory terminology, a subset of the sample space.

For example, when a cubical die is thrown, events of possible interest may be (a) that the score obtained is an even number, (b) that the score obtained is a multiple of 3.

An event will be denoted by a capital letter from the early part of the alphabet (A, B, C, …).

Example 1

A card is dealt from an ordinary pack of playing cards and its suit is to be noted. The sample space is S = {Hearts, Clubs, Diamonds, Spades}.

Examples of events in this case are

A = the dealt card will be red = {Hearts, Diamonds},

B = the dealt card will not be a Heart = {Clubs, Diamonds, Spades}.

Example 2

Two dice are thrown together and the sum of the scores is to be recorded. The sample space is S = {2, 3, 4, 5, 6, 7, 8, 9, 10, 11, 12}. Examples of events associated with this experiment are

A = the sum of the scores will be a perfect square = {4, 9},

B = the sum of the scores will be an even number = {2, 4, 6, 8, 10, 12}.

Example 3

A coin is tossed three times and the outcomes are to be recorded in the order that they occur. The sample space is

$$S = \{(HHH), (HHT), (HTH), (THH), (HTT), (THT), (TTH), (TTT)\},$$

where, for example, the element (THH) corresponds to the outcome that the first toss gives tail, the second gives head and the third gives head. Some examples of events in this case are:

A = exactly two heads will be tossed = {(HHT), (HTH), (THH)}

B = the third toss will give a head = {(HHH), (HTH), (THH), (TTH)}

C = all three tosses will have the same outcome = {(HHH), (TTT)}.

Definition. The *complement* of an event A, denoted by A′, is the event that "A will not occur". The elements of A′ will consist of all the elements of S that are not in A. For example, with A and B as defined in Example 2 above, we have

A′ = the sum of the scores will not be a perfect square = {2, 3, 5, 6, 7, 8, 10, 11, 12},

B′ = the sum of the scores will not be an even number = {3, 5, 7, 9, 11} (i.e. an odd number).

Combined events

Definitions. For any two events A and B

(a)　the event that "A or B or both occur" is called the *union* of A and B and will be written as A∪B;

(b)　the event that "both A and B will occur" is called the *intersection* of A and B and will be written as A∩B.

With A and B as defined in Example 2 we have

A∪B = the sum of the scores will be a perfect square <u>or</u> an even number

= {2, 4, 6, 8, 9, 10, 12},

obtained by pooling the elements of A and the elements of B.

A∩B = the sum of the scores will be a perfect square <u>and</u> an even number = {4},

obtained by listing those elements that are common to both A and B.

Example 4

For the events defined in Example 3 above, give a verbal description and list the elements of the events (a) A∪B, (b) A∩C, (c) A∩B'.

From Example 3 we have

S = {(HHH), (HHT), (HTH), (THH), (HTT), (THT), (TTH), (TTT)}

A = two heads will be tossed = {(HHT), (HTH), (THH)}

B = the third toss will be a head = {(HHH), (HTH), (THH), (TTH)}

C = the three tosses will have the same outcome = {(HHH), (TTT)}.

(a)　　A∪B = two heads will be tossed <u>or</u> the third toss will be a head

　　　　= {(HHT), (HTH), (THH), (HHH), (TTH)},

obtained by pooling the elements of A and B (i.e. by writing down the elements of A and then adding those elements of B that are not in A),

(b)　 A∩C = two heads will be tossed <u>and</u> the three tosses will have the same outcome.

We see that A and C have no element in common, so that A∩C cannot occur.

(c)　 A∩B' = two heads will be tossed <u>and</u> the third toss will not be a head.

B' = the third toss will not be a head = {(HHT), (HTT), (THT), (TTT)],

obtained by listing the elements of S that are not in B.

It follows that

　　　A∩B' = {(HHT)}, since (HHT) is the only common element in A and B'.

Definition. Two events which cannot occur at the same time are said to be **mutually exclusive**.

This means that there is no element in S which will result in both events occurring. A and C in Example 4 above are mutually exclusive events.

The union and intersection notation extends to more than two events in an obvious fashion. Thus, for three events A, B and C,

(a)　 A∪B∪C = at least one of A, B, C will occur,

whose elements are obtained by pooling the elements of all three events,

(b)　 A∩B∩C = all three events will occur,

whose elements will consist of all those elements which are common to A, B and C.

Example 5

With A, B and C as defined in Example 4 above, list the elements of (A∪B)∩C. In Example 4 we showed that

$$A∪B = \{(HHT), (HTH), (THH), (HHH), (TTH)\},$$

and C = {(HHH), (TTT)}.

Picking out the common elements we have (A∪B)∩C = {(HHH)}.

Exercise 3.2

1.   An ordinary cubical die is thrown. Let A denote the event that the score will be even, B the event that the score will be less than 3, and C the event that the score will be a multiple of 3.

(a)   List the elements of S, A, B and C. State which two events are mutually exclusive.

(b)   Give verbal descriptions and list the elements of the events

   (i) A′, (ii) A∩B, (iii) A∪C′, (iv) A∪B∪C, (v) (A∪B)∩C.

2.   A cubical die is thrown twice. Write down the sample space for the outcome, expressing each element as an ordered pair. Determine the elements of each of the events

(a)   A = the sum of the scores will be divisible by 4,

(b)   B = the scores will be the same,

(c)   C = both scores will be even,

(d)   D = the scores will differ by at least 4,

(e)   A∩C, (f) B∪D, (g) B∩A′.

   Which pairs (if any) of the events A, B, C and D are mutually exclusive?

3.   Two cards are dealt from a pack of 5 cards which are numbered from 1 to 5, and the sum of the two numbers dealt is recorded. Write down the 7 elements of the sample space and determine the elements of the events

(a)   A = the sum will be greater than 7,

(b)   B = the sum will be a prime number,

(c)   C = the sum will be an odd number,

(d)   A∪C,   (e) B∩C,   (f) A∩B′,   (g) (A∪B)′,   (h) A′∩B∩C.

3.3   Probabilities of events

Definition. The probability of an event associated with a random experiment is the <u>proportion</u> of times that the event will occur in an indefinitely large number of trials (performances) of the random experiment.

For an event which is bound to occur, the event will occur in every trial so that its probability is clearly equal to 1. In particular, regarding the sample space S as an event, we see that the probability of S occurring is given by $P(S) = 1$. Likewise for an event that cannot occur, its probability is 0. For example, when throwing a cubical die the event A = "a score which is a multiple of 7" cannot occur so that $P(A) = 0$. In particular if A and B are mutually exclusive then $P(A \cap B) = 0$. Since performing an experiment an indefinitely large number of times is not feasible in practice, an estimate of the probability of any other type of event is given by the proportion of times that the event occurs in a finite number of trials of the random experiment. The larger the number of trials, the closer we expect the estimate to be to the actual probability. In Statistics the proportion of times that an event occurs in several trials is called the *relative frequency* of the event in those trials. Suppose that in n trials of a random experiment the event A is observed to occur exactly r times. The relative frequency of A is $R_n(A) = r/n$, which provides an estimate of $P(A)$, the probability of A occurring in any future trial. Since A has occurred in r of the n trials it follows that A', the complement of A, has occurred n - r times, so that the relative frequency of A' in the n trials is given by

$$R_n(A') = \frac{n-r}{n} = 1 - \frac{r}{n} = 1 - R_n(A).$$

It is reasonable to suppose that this relationship will hold even for an indefinitely large number of trials. We thus have the following rule:

Rule 1:

For any event A, the probability that A will not occur is given by

$$\boxed{P(A') = 1 - P(A).}$$

Now consider two mutually exclusive events A and B. (Recall that mutually exclusive events are ones which cannot occur together). Suppose that in n trials the event A occurred r_A times and the event B occurred r_B times. It follows that $A \cup B$ (either A or B) occurred in $(r_A + r_B)$ of the trials, so that the relative frequency of $A \cup B$ in the n trials is

$$R_n(A \cup B) = \frac{r_A + r_B}{n} = R_n(A) + R_n(B),$$

which gives us the following rule:

Rule 2:

If A and B are mutually exclusive events then

$$\boxed{P(A \cup B) = P(A) + P(B).}$$

Now consider two events, A and B, that are not mutually exclusive. In n trials, suppose that A occurred r_A times, B occurred r_B times, and $A \cap B$ (both A and B) occurred r_{AB} times. Since each of r_A and r_B includes the r_{AB} times that $A \cap B$ occurred, the number of times that $A \cup B$ (A or B or both) occurred is $(r_A + r_B - r_{AB})$. Thus, the relative frequency of $A \cup B$ in the n trials is

$$R_n(A \cup B) = \frac{r_A + r_B - r_{AB}}{n} = R_n(A) + R_n(B) - R_n(A \cap B),$$

from which we have:

Rule 3:

For any two events A and B

$$P(A \cup B) = P(A) + P(B) - P(A \cap B).$$

Note that this reduces to Rule 2 when A and B are mutually exclusive.

The above rules can also be demonstrated using *Venn* diagrams. In a Venn diagram a rectangle is drawn to represent the sample space S. Imagine that all the outcomes of a random experiment are scattered as points throughout this rectangle. We use areas to represent probabilities. Since $P(S) = 1$ we take the rectangle to have unit area. Now let A denote an event which is represented by the circle shown in Figure 1. The scattering of the outcomes in the rectangle is assumed to have been such that all the elements of A are inside the circle. The area of this circle represents P(A). Since all the elements of A' are outside the circle A it follows that $P(A') = 1 - P(A)$, as illustrated in Figure 1.

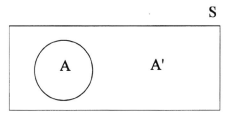

Figure 1. $P(A') = 1 - P(A)$

Figure 2 illustrates two events A and B that are mutually exclusive. Consideration of areas shows that $P(A \cup B) = P(A) + P(B)$ as given by Rule 2 above.

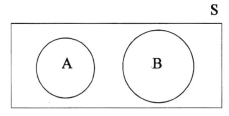

Figure 2. $P(A \cup B) = P(A) + P(B)$

Figure 3 illustrates two events A and B that are not mutually exclusive. The overlapping (shaded) region of the two circles represents A∩B and includes all the outcomes which are elements common to A and B. The area of this overlap is P(A∩B) and it is seen from the diagram that P(A∪B) = P(A) + P(B) – P(A∩B), as stated in Rule 3.

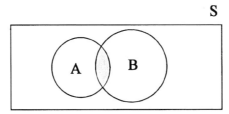

Figure 3. P(A∪B) = P(A) + P(B) – P(A∩B)

Consideration of relative frequencies or Venn diagrams can produce more rules for probabilities. Two additional rules are given below.

Rule 4

For any two events A and B

$$P(A∩B') = P(A) – P(A∩B).$$

This is illustrated in Figure 4. Note that the region in the circle A excluding the overlap includes all the outcomes which are elements of A but not elements of B; that is, the event A∩B'. Note also that P(A∩B') is the probability that A will occur and B will not occur.

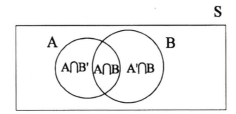

Figure 4. P(A∩B') = P(A) – P(A∩B)

Similarly, the probability that B will occur and A will not occur is given by

$$P(A'∩B) = P(B) – P(A∩B)$$

Rule 5:

For any two events A and B,

$$P(A'∩B') = 1 – P(A∪B)$$

This follows from Rule 1 on noting that A'∩B' is the complement of A∪B, and is illustrated in Figure 5, where A'∩B' is the region outside the circles A and B.

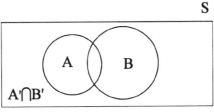

Figure 5. $P(A' \cap B') = 1 - P(A \cup B)$

Example 1.

The two events A and B are such that

$$P(A) = 0.6, \quad P(B) = 0.3, \quad \text{and} \quad P(A \cap B) = 0.2.$$

Evaluate (a) $P(A')$, (b) $P(A \cup B)$, (c) $P(A \cap B')$, (d) the probability that only one of A and B will occur.

Solution

(a)   Using Rule 1 we have

$$P(A') = 1 - P(A) = 1 - 0.6 = 0.4$$

(b)   Using Rule 3 we have

$$P(A \cup B) = P(A) + P(B) - P(A \cap B)$$
$$= 0.6 + 0.3 - 0.2 = 0.7.$$

(c)   Using Rule 4 we have

$$P(A \cap B') = P(A) - P(A \cap B) = 0.6 - 0.2 = 0.4$$

(d)   The event "only one of A and B" will occur if either (i) A occurs and B does not occur $(A \cap B')$ or (ii) A does not occur and B does occur $(A' \cap B)$.

That is,   only one of A and B = $(A \cap B') \cup (A' \cap B)$.

Since $A \cap B'$ and $A' \cap B$ are mutually exclusive events it follows from Rule 2 that

$$P(\text{only one will occur}) = P(A \cap B') + P(A' \cap B) = 0.4 + P(A' \cap B).$$

Using Rule 4 (interchanging A and B) we have

$$P(A' \cap B) = P(B) - P(A \cap B) = 0.3 - 0.2 = 0.1.$$

It follows that P(only one will occur)= $0.4 + 0.1 = 0.5$

Alternatively, $P(A \cap B') + P(A' \cap B) = P(A) - P(A \cap B) + P(B) - P(A \cap B)$
$$= P(A) + P(B) - 2P(A \cap B)$$
$$= 0.6 + 0.3 - 2 \times 0.2 = 0.5$$

The Venn diagram for answering Example 1 is shown below.

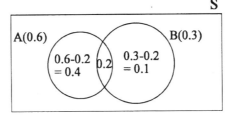

Probability

Example 2.

A and B are two events such that
$$P(A) = P(B) = p, \quad P(A \cap B) = 0.4, \text{ and } P(A \cup B) = 0.7.$$
Evaluate (a) p, (b) $P(A' \cap B)$, (c) $P(A' \cap B')$.

Solution

(a) Using Rule 3
$$P(A \cup B) = P(A) + P(B) - P(A \cap B)$$
$$0.7 = p + p - 0.4 = 2p - 0.4,$$
from which it follows that $2p = 0.7 + 0.4 = 1.1$, so that $p = 1.1/2 = 0.55$.

(b) Using Rule 4
$$P(A' \cap B) = P(B) - P(A \cap B) = 0.55 - 0.4 = 0.15$$

(c) Using Rule 5
$$P(A' \cap B') = 1 - P(A \cup B) = 1 - 0.7 = 0.3$$

The Venn diagram for answering this example is shown below.

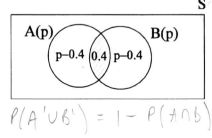

$$P(A' \cup B') = 1 - P(A \cap B)$$

Exercise 3.3

1. A and B are two events such that
$$P(A) = 0.7, \quad P(B) = 0.2, \text{ and } P(A \cap B) = 0.1.$$
   Evaluate (a) $P(A')$, (b) $P(A \cup B)$, (c) $P(A \cap B')$.

2. A and B are mutually exclusive events such that
$$P(A) = 0.5 \text{ and } P(B) = 0.1.$$
   Evaluate (a) $P(A \cup B)$, (b) $P(A' \cap B')$, (c) $P(A' \cup B')$.

3. The events A and B are such that
$$P(A) = 0.4, \quad P(B) = 0.3, \text{ and } P(A \cup B) = 0.58.$$
   Evaluate (a) $P(A \cap B)$, (b) $P(A' \cap B)$, (c) $P(A' \cup B)$.

4. A and B are two events such that $P(A) = 0.25$, $P(B) = 0.40$ and $P(A \cap B) = 0.15$.
   Find (a) $P(A')$, (b) $P(A \cup B)$, (c) $P(A' \cap B')$, (d) $P(A \cap B')$, (e) $P(A' \cap B)$.

5. A and B are two events such that $P(A) = 0.36$, $P(B) = 0.25$, $P(A \cap B') = 0.24$.
   Evaluate (a) $P(A')$, (b) $P(A \cap B)$, (c) $P(A' \cap B)$, (d) the probability that only one of A and B will occur.

6. A, B and C are three events with A and B being mutually exclusive and such that P(A) = 0.4, P(B) = 0.3, P(C) = 0.2, P(B∩C) = 0.1, and P(A∩C) = 0.08. By means of a Venn diagram, or otherwise, evaluate (a) P(A'∩C), (b) P(B∪C), (c) P(A∪B∪C), (d) the probability that none of the events A, B and C will occur.

7. The events A, B and C are such that
$$P(A) = \tfrac{1}{2}, \ P(B) = \tfrac{1}{3}, P(C) = \tfrac{1}{4} \text{ and } P(A∩B) = \tfrac{1}{6}.$$
Calculate (a) P(A'∪B'), (b) P(A'∩B'), (c) P(A∩B). $1 - P(A∩B)$
(d) Given that A and C are mutually exclusive and that B and C are mutually exclusive, calculate P(A∪B∪C).

3.4 Equally likely outcomes

In some random experiments it is reasonable to suppose that all the possible outcomes are equally likely to occur so that each outcome has the same probability of occurring. Examples of such random experiments are as follows:

(1) Throwing a cubical die which is known to be fair (i.e. perfectly balanced), in which case each possible score has the same probability of occurring, namely 1/6.

(2) Dealing a card from a shuffled pack of ordinary playing cards, so that each card has the same probability (1/52) of being dealt.

(3) Making a 'blind' selection of one object from a collection of objects, so that each object in the collection has the same probability of being chosen. Such a 'blind' selection will be referred to as a *random selection*.

Consider a random experiment having sample space S consisting of N elements and that a trial of the experiment is to be performed in such a way that it is reasonable to suppose that the outcome is equally likely to be any one of the N possible outcomes. This means that each possible outcome has probability 1/N of occurring. Let A denote an event which consists of n(A) elements, so that A occurs if the outcome is one of the n(A) elements of A. It is then reasonable to define the probability that A will occur in a trial of the random experiment as

$$P(A) = \frac{n(A)}{N}.$$

Example 1

One card is drawn at random from a pack of 20 cards numbered from 1 to 20. Let A denote the event that the number on the chosen card will be a multiple of 5 and let B denote the event that the number on the chosen card will be greater than 14. Evaluate:

(a) P(A),   (b) P(B),   (c) P(A∩B),   (d) P(A∪B),   (e) P(A'∩B).

Solution

Since the card is drawn at random the chosen number is equally likely to be any one of the 20 numbers, so that N = 20.

(a)   A = a multiple of 5 = {5, 10, 15, 20}, so that n(A) = 4 and P(A) = 4/20 = 1/5.

(b)   B = greater than 14 = {15, 16, 17, 18, 19, 20}, so that n(B) = 6 and P(B) = 6/20 = 3/10.

(c)   Picking out the elements common to A and B we find that

A∩B = {15, 20}, so that n(A∩B) = 2 and P(A∩B) = 2/20 = 1/10.

(d)   Pooling the elements of A and B we have

A∪B = {5, 10, 15, 16, 17,18, 19, 20}, so that n(A∪B) = 8 and P(A∪B) = 8/20 = 2/5.

(e)   Picking out the elements in B which are not in A we have

A'∩B = {16, 17, 18, 19}, so that n(A'∩B) = 4 and P(A'∩B) = 4/20 = 1/5.

[Alternatively, using Rule 4 and the answers to (b) and (c)

$$P(A' \cap B) = P(B) - P(A \cap B) = 6/20 - 2/20 = 4/20 = 1/5].$$

Example 2

A fair coin is tossed three times. Find the probability that the outcome will be (a) three heads, (b) at least one head, (c) one head or one tail.

Solution

Since the coin is fair we can assume that all possible outcomes are equally likely to occur. The sample space for the ordered outcomes of the three tosses is

$$S = \{(HHH), (HHT), (HTH), (THH), (HTT), (THT), (TTH), (TTT)\}$$

so that the total number of outcomes is N = 8, which are equally likely.

(a)   Let A denote the event that three heads will be obtained. Then

A = {(HHH)} so that n(A) = 1. It follows that P(A) = 1/8.

(b)   Let B denote the event that at least one head will be obtained. Then

B = {(HHH), (HHT), (HTH), (THH), (HTT), (THT), (TTH)}, and n(B) = 7, so that P(B) = 7/8.

[Alternatively, note that the complement of B is B' = no head = {(TTT)}, so that n(B') = 1 and P(B') = 1/8. Using Rule 1 we then have

$$P(B) = 1 - P(B') = 1 - 1/8 = 7/8]$$

(c)   Let C denote the event that one head or one tail will be obtained. We see that C ={(HHT), (HTH), (THH), (HTT), (THT), (TTH)}, so that

n(C) = 6 and P(C) = 6/8 = 3/4.

[Alternatively, let C_1 denote the event "one head" and C_2 the event "one tail". Noting that C = $C_1 \cup C_2$ and that C_1 and C_2 are mutually exclusive it follows from Rule 2 that

$$P(C) = P(C_1) + P(C_2) = 3/8 + 3/8 = 6/8 = 3/4].$$

Exercise 3.4a

1. One card is drawn at random from 13 cards numbered from 1 to 13. Calculate the probability that the number on the chosen card will be (a) less than 5, (b) a multiple of 4, (c) a perfect square, (d) a perfect square or a multiple of 4, (e) a perfect square <u>and</u> greater than 5.

2. In a sixth form of 20 pupils, 5 are studying Mathematics, 4 are studying Physics and 2 are studying both Mathematics and Physics. Find the probability that a randomly chosen pupil from this form is studying Mathematics or Physics or both. [Hint: Draw a Venn diagram].

3. A cubical die has two faces numbered 1, two faces numbered 2, and the remaining two faces numbered 3. When the die is thrown, the score obtained is the number on the uppermost face. This die is to be thrown twice. Calculate the probability that (a) the score on the first throw will be 3 and on the second throw will be less than 3, (b) at least one of the two scores will be 2, (c) the sum of the two scores will be 4.

4. A fair cubical die with its faces numbered from 1 to 6 is to be thrown twice. Calculate the probability that (a) the sum of the two scores will be (i) 6, (ii) 7, (b) the product of the two scores obtained will be at least 10, (c) one of the scores obtained will be exactly 2 more than the other score. [Hint: As indicated in Example 4 of Section 3.1 the sample space will have 36 elements].

Counting Aids

In Example 2 above we listed all the possible ordered outcomes when tossing a fair coin three times and determined N by counting how many there were. Listing all the possible outcomes of a random experiment can be very tedious as, for example, if a coin or a die is tossed six or more times. It would be advantageous to have a method for determining N without having to list all the possible outcomes. To illustrate such a method, suppose a cubical die is thrown twice. Each outcome will be an ordered pair, consisting of the score obtained on the first throw followed by the score obtained on the second throw. Each of the 6 possible scores on the first throw has to be paired with each of the 6 possible scores on the second throw so that the total number of ordered pairs is $6 \times 6 = 36$. Now, if the die is thrown three times, each of these 36 ordered pairs has to be combined with each of the 6 possible scores on the third throw, so that the number of possible outcomes (ordered triples) of the three throws is $36 \times 6 = 216$. This method can also be useful for finding the number of elements n(A) of an event A. Generalising, we have:

The multiplication principle

If k random experiments are performed simultaneously or in sequence and the ith experiment has N_i possible outcomes (i = 1, 2, ..., k) then the number of possible *ordered* outcomes of all k experiments is $N_1 \times N_2 \times ... \times N_k$.

Example 3

Two cards are dealt from a shuffled pack of ordinary playing cards. Find the probability that at least one of the two cards is an ace.

Solution

Let A denote the event that there will be at least one ace. The complement of A is the event A′ that no ace is dealt. [It turns out here that it is easier to evaluate P(A′) than P(A)].

The first card dealt may be any one of the 52 cards in the pack and the second may be any one of the 51 cards remaining in the pack. Using the multiplication principle the total number of possible paired outcomes for the two cards dealt is N = 52 × 51 = 2652. [With such a large number it is as well that we can avoid having to list all the elements of S].

Now consider A′, that neither card is an ace. Since 48 of the 52 cards in the pack are not aces, the event A′ occurs if the first card is any one of those 48 cards and the second is any one of the 47 non-aces remaining in the pack. Using the multiplication principle, we have n(A′) = 48 × 47 = 2256. It follows that

$$P(A') = \frac{2256}{2652} = \frac{188}{221} ,$$

and using Rule 1

$$P(A) = 1 - P(A') = 1 - \frac{188}{221} = \frac{33}{221} .$$

[Alternatively, we could write $A = A_1 \cup A_2$, where A_1 denotes the event that exactly one ace is dealt, and A_2 denotes the event that two aces are dealt. On noting that A_1 and A_2 are mutually exclusive it follows from Rule 2 that $P(A) = P(A_1) + P(A_2)$. It is left as an exercise to show that this gives the same answer as obtained above. [You will need to note that A_1 occurs if the outcome is (Ace, non-Ace) or (non-Ace, Ace)].

Example 4 (The classical birthday problem)

Find the probability that at least two people in a group of n people have birthdays on the same day.

Solution

Ignoring the possibility that a person was born on 29 February, we shall assume that each person's birthday is equally likely to be on any one of the 365 days in a year. The days on which the n persons have their birthdays will be an n-tuple $(d_1, d_2, d_3, \ldots, d_n)$, where each d_i is one of the integers from 1 to 365. Using the multiplication principle, the number of such n-tuples is $N = 365^n$.

Let A denote the event that at least two of the d_i are the same (i.e. that at least two of the persons share the same birthday). The complementary event A' is that all the d_i are different (i.e. no two of the persons share the same birthday). It so happens that it is much easier to find n(A') than n(A). Every element of A' is such that all the d_i are different so that $n(A') = 365 \times 364 \times \ldots (366 - n)$, provided n < 366. (For $n \geq 366$, the probability is 1 that there will be at least two persons sharing the same birthday). It follows that

$$P(A') = \frac{365 \times 364 \times \ldots \times (366 - n)}{365^n}$$

and $P(A) = 1 - P(A')$.

The following table gives the values of P(A) for some selected values of n.

n	10	20	22	23	30	40	50	60
P(A)	0.117	0.411	0.476	0.507	0.706	0.891	0.971	0.984

We see that a group of at least 23 persons is more likely than not to include at least two people sharing the same birthday, and that a group of 50 or more is almost certain to include at least two people sharing the same birthday.

Exercise 3.4b

1. One card is dealt from a shuffled pack of ordinary playing cards. It is replaced in the pack which is then shuffled and a card is dealt from it. Calculate the probabilities that (a) the first card is an ace, (b) at least one of the two cards dealt is an ace. [Compare your answers with those obtained in Example 3 above].

2. A fair cubical die has two of its faces numbered 1, two numbered 2 and two numbered 3. When the die is thrown the score obtained is the number on the uppermost face. Given that the die is thrown three times, calculate the probability that the three scores obtained (a) will be equal, (b) will sum to 6.

3. Stating any assumptions that you make, find an expression for the probability that in a group of n people at least two of them share the same birthmonth. Deduce the smallest n for which the group is more likely than not to include at least two people sharing the same birthmonth.

4. Three fair cubical dice are tossed together. Find the probability that the three scores will be such that (a) they are all different (b) they are three consecutive integers.

5. Two balls are drawn at random, one after another, from a bag which contains 10 red, 30 white and 20 blue balls. Calculate the probability that (a) both balls will be white, (b) the first ball will be white and the second blue, (c) at least one blue ball will be drawn.

6. Repeat Question 5 if the first ball drawn is replaced in the bag before the second ball is drawn.

7. Two cards are to be drawn at random from a pack of 15 cards which are numbered from 1 to 15, respectively. For each of the cases when the drawing is made (i) with replacement, and (ii) without replacement, calculate the probability that (a) the first number drawn will be less than 10 and the second drawn will be greater than 9, (b) the sum of the two numbers drawn will be 8.

8. A tetrahedral die has its four faces marked with the numbers 1, 2, 3 and 4, respectively. When the die is thrown onto a hard surface the score obtained is the number on the face in contact with the surface, which is equally likely to be any one of the four faces. The die is thrown twice. Calculate the probability that

(a) the sum of the two scores will be 5,

(b) the difference between the two scores will be 1,

(c) the product of the two scores will be 4.

Unordered outcomes

In the above we took account of the order in which outcomes were obtained when two or more random experiments were performed simultaneously or in sequence. In many problems the actual order is not important. This is certainly so in many card games where it is the composition of a dealt hand which is relevant and not the order in which the cards were dealt. If a sample of k objects is drawn without replacement from a collection of n objects and the order in which they are drawn is unimportant, then we refer to the drawn k objects as an *unordered sample of size* k. Clearly, the sample space for an unordered sample of a given size will be smaller (i.e. will contain fewer elements) than when order is taken into account.

Example 5

Three cards are dealt from a pack of six cards numbered from 1 to 6. Find the number of different combinations of numbers that are possible. The outcomes will consist of all possible combinations of three different numbers chosen from 1 to 6. These are

$\{1, 2, 3\}$, $\{1, 2, 4\}$, $\{1, 2, 5\}$, $\{1, 2, 6\}$, $\{1, 3, 4\}$, $\{1, 3, 5\}$, $\{1, 3, 6\}$, $\{1, 4, 5\}$,
$\{1, 4, 6\}$, $\{1, 5, 6\}$, $\{2, 3, 4\}$, $\{2, 3, 5\}$, $\{2, 3, 6\}$, $\{2, 4, 5\}$, $\{2, 4, 6\}$, $\{2, 5, 6\}$,
$\{3, 4, 5\}$, $\{3, 4, 6\}$, $\{3, 5, 6\}$, $\{4, 5, 6\}$.

We see that there are 20 possible combinations of three different numbers. This method of listing all possibilities is clearly very tedious especially when dealing with numbers larger than the 3 and 6 in the above example. Consider one of the combinations in the above example, say {1, 2, 3}. The number of different orders in which this particular combination could have arisen is $3 \times 2 = 6$, since the first number dealt could be any one of 1, 2, 3 and the second any of the other two numbers with no choice remaining for the third number dealt. Similarly, every one of the above combinations could arise from six different orderings. It follows that the number of different combinations is exactly 1/6 of the total number of ordered outcomes. Now, the number of ordered outcomes is $6 \times 5 \times 4 = 120$, and it follows that the number of different combinations is 120/6 = 20, as listed above.

The following example considers a situation where the listing of all possibilities would be prohibitive.

Example 6

Find the total number of different hands when 9 cards are dealt from a shuffled pack of ordinary playing cards.

Solution

The number of *ordered* ways in which a particular hand of 9 cards could be dealt is

$$9 \times 8 \times 7 \times 6 \times 5 \times 4 \times 3 \times 2 \times 1,$$

which we write as 9! (pronounced as 9 factorial or factorial 9). It follows that each hand of 9 cards can arise from 9! different orders in which the cards are dealt. When ordering is taken into account the total number of possibilities is

$$52 \times 51 \times 50 \times 49 \times 48 \times 47 \times 46 \times 45 \times 44 = \frac{52!}{43!},$$

where $n! = n \times (n-1) \times (n-2) \times \ldots \times 3 \times 2 \times 1$.

It follows that the number of different hands is

$$\frac{52!}{43!} \div 9! = \frac{52!}{43! \times 9!},$$

which is written as $\binom{52}{9}$ or as $^{52}C_9$. Most calculators will have a key labelled n! (or x!) and another labelled ^nC_r. The actual value of $^{52}C_9$ is 3 679 075 400.

In general we have the following result:

The total number of unordered samples of r objects chosen without replacement from a collection of n objects is

$$\binom{n}{r} = \frac{n!}{r! \times (n-r)!}$$

Example 7

A box contains 5 red, 7 blue and 8 white balls. Three balls are drawn at random (without replacement) from this box. Calculate the probability that the drawn balls will be such that (a) two are red and one is blue, (b) no two are of the same colour, (c) all three are of the same colour.

Solution

Since the box contains 20 balls the total number of combinations of the three balls is

$$N = \binom{20}{3} = 1140,$$ which are equally probable.

(a) Let A denote the event that 2 red and 1 blue are drawn. The number of ways of choosing 2 red balls from 5 is $\binom{5}{2} = 10$ and the number of ways of choosing 1 blue ball from 7 is $\binom{7}{1} = 7$. Since each choice of 2 red balls can be combined with each choice of blue ball we have

$$n(A) = 10 \times 7 = 70,$$

and

$$P(A) = \frac{70}{1140} = \frac{7}{114}.$$

(b) Let B denote the event that the balls drawn are of different colours; that is, 1 red from 5, 1 blue from 7 and 1 white from 8. The number of ways in which this can arise is

$$n(B) = \binom{5}{1} \times \binom{7}{1} \times \binom{8}{1} = 5 \times 7 \times 8 = 280$$

and so

$$P(B) = \frac{280}{1140} = \frac{14}{57}.$$

(c) Let C denote the event that the drawn balls are of the same colour. We may write

$$C = C_R \cup C_B \cup C_W,$$

where C_R is the event that all three are red, C_B the event that all three are blue, and C_W the event that all three are white. On noting that these events are mutually exclusive we have $P(C) = P(C_R) + P(C_B) + P(C_W)$. Also

$$n(C_R) = \binom{5}{3} = 10, \ n(C_B) = \binom{7}{3} = 35, \ n(C_W) = \binom{8}{3} = 56$$

It follows that

$$P(C) = \frac{10 + 35 + 56}{1140} = \frac{101}{1140}.$$

Exercise 3.4c

1. A box contains 5 red, 4 white and 3 blue balls. Three balls are drawn at random (without replacement). Calculate the probability that (a) 3 red balls will be drawn, (b) 3 balls of the same colour will be drawn, (c) at least one red ball will be drawn.

2. A committee consists of 6 men and 4 women. A subcommittee of 4 is to be drawn at random. Calculate the probability that (a) 4 men will be chosen, (b) 2 men and 2 women will be chosen, (c) more men than women will be chosen.

3. Four cards are drawn at random (without replacement) from a pack of 8 cards numbered from 1 to 8. Calculate the probability that (a) both 1 and 8 will be drawn, (b) the largest number drawn will be 6, (c) two even and two odd numbers will be drawn.

4. A hand of three cards is dealt from a shuffled pack of ordinary playing cards. Calculate the probability that the hand will consist of (a) 3 kings, (b) 2 aces and 1 king, (c) 1 ace, 1 king and 1 queen.

5. Four numbers are chosen at random (without replacement) from a collection of 11 numbers, 6 of which are positive and 5 are negative. Calculate the probability that the product of the four chosen numbers will be positive.

6. A subcommittee of 3 is chosen at random from a committee of 10 women, 2 of whom are sisters. Calculate the probability that the subcommittee will include (a) one and only one of the two sisters, (b) both sisters.

7. All the spades have been withdrawn from a pack of ordinary playing cards, leaving a pack of 39 cards (13 hearts, 13 clubs and 13 diamonds). This pack is shuffled and 5 cards are dealt. Calculate the probability that the 5 cards dealt will consist of (a) 2 hearts, 2 clubs and 1 diamond, (b) aces and kings only, (c) no ace, no king, no queen and no jack.

8. Of the 12 sweets in a packet, 5 are chocolates and 7 are toffees Six of the sweets are chosen at random. Calculate the probability that
   (a) all 6 of the chosen sweets are toffees
   (b) exactly two of the chosen sweets are chocolates
   (c) the majority of the chosen sweets are toffees.

3.5 Conditional probability

Example 1

One card was chosen at random from a pack of 7 cards which are numbered from 1 to 7. Given that the chosen number was even, what is the probability that the chosen number was a multiple of 3?

Solution

The sample space for the chosen number is S = {1, 2, 3, 4, 5, 6, 7}. Let A denote the event that the chosen number is even. Since we are given that the chosen number was even, the *effective* sample space for the outcome is actually A = {2, 4, 6}, the elements of which are equally probable. Let B denote the event that the chosen number is a multiple of 3. Knowing that A has occurred, B will also have occurred only if the chosen number was 6. Since n(A) = 3 it follows that the probability that the chosen number was a multiple of 3 is $\frac{1}{3}$.

This is a simple example of a conditional probability, the conditioning being the given information that the chosen number was even. We shall write P(B|A) for the conditional probability that B occurred given that A occurred. In the above example P(B|A) = $\frac{1}{3}$.

Now consider the general case of a random experiment having been performed and we are given that the event A has occurred. It follows that the actual outcome was an element of A. We may now be interested in finding P(B|A), the probability that B has also occurred.

Recalling the relative frequency interpretation of a probability, P(B|A) is the limiting value of the relative frequency of B in those trials in which A occurred. Suppose that in n trials of the random experiment, A was observed to occur r_A times, B was observed to occur r_B times, and both A and B was observed to occur r_{AB} times. Then, for the r_A trials in which A occurred, the relative frequency of B is given by

$$R_n(B|A) = \frac{r_{AB}}{r_A} \equiv \frac{r_{AB}/n}{r_A/n} \equiv \frac{R_n(A \cap B)}{R_n(A)} .$$

Allowing n to increase indefinitely, the relative frequencies may be replaced by probabilities to give

$$P(B|A) = \frac{P(A \cap B)}{P(A)} . \tag{1}$$

We take this as a general definition of P(B|A) for any random experiment irrespective of whether or not its outcomes are equally likely, provided P(A) ≠ 0.

In Example 1 above S = {1, 2, 3, 4, 5, 6, 7}, A = {2, 4, 6} and B = {3, 6}, so that A∩B = {6}. It follows that n(A∩B) = 1, so that P(A∩B) = $\frac{1}{7}$, and n(A) = 3 so that P(A) = $\frac{3}{7}$.

Hence, $P(B \mid A) = \dfrac{1/7}{3/7} = \dfrac{1}{3}$, as obtained earlier.

Interchanging A and B in (1) above, the conditional probability of A, given that B has occurred is

$$P(A|B) = \frac{P(A \cap B)}{P(B)}. \tag{2}$$

Combining both results we have

$$P(A \cap B) = P(B|A)P(A) = P(A|B)P(B), \tag{3}$$

provided that $P(A) \neq 0$ and $P(B) \neq 0$.

Example 2

A subcommittee of five people was chosen at random from a committee consisting of 10 men and 8 women. Given that the chosen subcommittee included at least one woman, calculate the conditional probability that exactly two women were chosen.

Solution

The total number of combinations for the composition of the subcommittee is

$$N = \binom{18}{5} = 8568 ,$$

which are equally probable because the selection was made at random. Let A denote the event that at least one woman is chosen and let B denote the event that 2 women are chosen. We need to find $P(B|A)$. On using definition (1) above

$$P(B|A) = \frac{P(A \cap B)}{P(A)}.$$

To determine $P(A)$ we shall first determine $P(A')$, where A' is the event that no woman is chosen. A' occurs if only men are chosen and we see that

$$n(A') = \binom{10}{5} = 252.$$

It follows that $P(A') = 252/8568$, and therefore, $P(A) = 1 - P(A') = 8316/8568$. Now, the event $A \cap B$ occurs if the subcommittee consists of at least one woman and exactly two women, which is equivalent to exactly two women being chosen, so that $A \cap B$ occurs if two women and three men are chosen. The number of ways this can occur is

$$n(A \cap B) = \binom{10}{3} \times \binom{8}{2} = 120 \times 28 = 3360 .$$

Thus,

$$P(A \cap B) = \frac{3360}{8568},$$

and we find

$$P(A|B) = \frac{3360 / 8568}{8316 / 8568} = \frac{3360}{8316} = \frac{40}{99}.$$

Example 3

A and B are two events such that $P(A) = 0.4$, $P(B) = 0.3$, and $P(B|A) = 0.5$.
Evaluate (a) $P(A \cap B)$, (b) $P(A|B)$, (c) $P(B'|A)$, (d) $P(A'|B')$.

Solution

(a) From (3)

$$P(A \cap B) = P(B|A)P(A) = 0.5 \times 0.4 = 0.2.$$

(b) From (2)

$$P(A|B) = \frac{P(A \cap B)}{P(B)} = \frac{0.2}{0.3} = \frac{2}{3}$$

(c) By Rule 1 $P(B'|A) = 1 - P(B|A) = 0.5$

(d) From the definintion of a conditional probability we have

$$P(A'|B') = \frac{P(A' \cap B')}{P(B')}.$$

Now,

$$P(A' \cap B') = 1 - P(A \cup B)$$
$$= 1 - \{P(A) + P(B) - (P(A \cap B))\}$$
$$= 1 - (0.4 + 0.3 - 0.2) = 0.5.$$

Also $P(B') = 1 - P(B) = 1 - 0.3 = 0.7.$

Therefore

$$P(A'|B') = \frac{0.5}{0.7} = \frac{5}{7}.$$

Exercise 3.5

1. Two balls are drawn at random from a box containing 10 balls, of which 7 are black. Given that the first ball drawn was black, calculate the conditional probability that the second ball drawn was also black.

2. A fair coin was tossed three times. Given that the first two tosses fell alike (i.e. both heads or both tails) calculate the conditional probability that the third toss gave a head.

3. A box contains three red balls numbered 1, 2, 3, respectively, and two white balls numbered 1 and 2, respectively. Two balls were drawn at random without replacement from this box. Find the conditional probability that both balls drawn were white given that (a) at least one of the balls drawn was white, (b) one of the balls drawn was the white ball numbered 1.

4. A and B are two events such that $P(A) = 0.5$, $P(B) = 0.3$ and $P(A \cap B) = 0.2$. Evaluate (a) $P(A|B)$, (b) $P(B|A)$, (c) $P(A'|B)$, (d) $P(A'|B')$.

5. Four cards were dealt at random from a pack of 8 cards numbered from 1 to 8 respectively. Given that the largest number dealt was 7, calculate the conditional probability that the smallest number dealt was 3.

6. A family includes 4 boys and 4 girls. Two of the children are chosen at random. (a) Given that at least one of those chosen was a girl, calculate the conditional probability that both were girls. (b) Given that one of the two chosen was the youngest girl, calculate the conditional probability that the other one chosen was a girl.

7. Three events A, B and C are such that $P(A) = 0.4$, $P(B) = 0.3$ and $P(C) = 0.5$. Given that $P(A \cap C) = 0.2$ and $P(B \cap C) = 0.25$, find the values of (a) $P(C|B)$, (b) $P(A' \cap C')$.

8. Five balls are drawn at random without replacement from a bag which contains 6 red balls, 5 blue balls and 4 white balls. (a) Given that exactly 2 of the drawn balls were red, calculate the conditional probability that the other 3 were 2 blue balls and 1 white ball. (b) Given that all 5 balls were of the same colour, calculate the conditional probability that they were red.

9. Two fair dice are thrown. Given that the total score was even, calculate the conditional probability that the scores on both dice were even.

10. A class contains 30 pupils. Of these 15 study French, 17 study Economics and 5 study both these subjects. A member of the class is chosen at random. Let F denote the event that the chosen pupil is studying French and let E denote the event that the chosen pupil is studying Economics. Calculate (a) $P(F)$ (b) $P(F|E)$ (c) $P(F|E')$.

3.6 Total Probability and Bayes' formula

Recall that events A_1, A_2, …, A_r are said to be mutually exclusive if no two of them can occur at the same time. Such events are also said to be *exhaustive* if every possible outcome of the associated random experiment is an element of one and only one of the events. The following Venn diagram illustrates three events which are mutually exclusive and exhaustive.

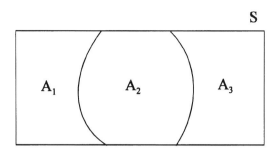

Figure 6 Mutually exclusive and exhaustive events

For any event A, note that A and A' are mutually exclusive and exhaustive. Let B be some other event. Then B can only occur in conjunction with either A or A'. That is

$$B = (A \cap B) \cup (A' \cap B).$$

Since (A∩B) and (A'∩B) are mutually exclusive it follows that

$$P(B) = P(A \cap B) + P(A' \cap B).$$
$$= P(B|A)P(A) + P(B|A')P(A').$$

Now consider three events A_1, A_2, A_3 which are mutually exclusive and exhaustive, and let B denote some other event. For B to occur it has to be in conjunction with one of A_1, A_2, A_3. That is,

$$B = (A_1 \cap B) \cup (A_2 \cap B) \cup (A_3 \cap B),$$

so that

$$P(B) = P(A_1 \cap B) + P(A_2 \cap B) + (A_3 \cap B)$$
$$= P(B|A_1)P(A_1) + P(B|A_2)P(A_2) + P(B|A_3)P(A_3).$$

Generalising, we have the following rule, called the rule of *Total Probability*.

RULE 6:

If A_1, A_2, …, A_r are mutually exclusive and exhaustive events and B is any other event, then

$$P(B) = P(B|A_1)P(A_1) + P(B|A_2)P(A_2) + … + P(B|A_r)P(A_r).$$

Example 1

Two balls are to be drawn at random without replacement from a box containing 12 red balls and 8 blue balls. Calculate the probability that the second ball drawn will be blue.

Solution

Let A denote the event that the first ball drawn will be blue, so that A' is the event that the first ball drawn will be red. Let B denote the event that the second ball drawn will be blue. Since A and A' are mutually exclusive and exhaustive it follows from Rule 6 that

$$P(B) = P(B|A)P(A) + P(B|A')P(A').$$

$P(A) =$ the probability that the first ball drawn will be blue $= 8/20$ so that $P(A') = 1 - P(A) = 12/20$.

$P(B|A)$ is the probability that the second ball will be blue given that the first ball was blue. If the first ball was blue then for the second draw the bag contains 12 red and 7 blue balls so that $P(B|A) = 7/19$. Similarly, if the first ball was red then for the second draw the bag contains 11 red and 8 blue balls, so that $P(B|A') = 8/19$.

Hence,
$$P(B) = \frac{7}{19} \times \frac{8}{20} + \frac{8}{19} \times \frac{12}{20} = \frac{8}{20}.$$

which is precisely the probability that the first ball drawn will be blue.

[Offer a simple explanation why this is so].

Example 2

Of the total daily output of a specific type of article at a factory, 40% are produced on machine A, 10% on machine B, and 50% on machine C. Of the articles produced on machine A, 60% are red and 40% are green. Of the articles produced on machine B, 30% are red and 70% are green. Of the articles produced on machine C, 50% are red and 50% are green. (a) Calculate the probability that an article chosen at random from a day's total output will be green. (b) Given that the chosen article was green, calculate the conditional probability that it was produced on machine A.

Solution

(a) Let A denote the event that the chosen article was produced on machine A, B the event that it was produced on machine B, and C the event that it was produced on machine C. The events A, B and C are mutually exclusive and exhaustive and from the information given
$$P(A) = 0.4, \ P(B) = 0.1, \ P(C) = 0.5.$$

Let G denote the event that the chosen article is green. From the information given we have
$$P(G|A) = 0.4, \ P(G|B) = 0.7, \ P(G|C) = 0.5.$$

Using Rule 6 we have
$$P(G) = P(G|A)P(A) + P(G|B)P(B) + P(G|C)P(C)$$
$$= 0.4 \times 0.4 + 0.7 \times 0.1 + 0.5 \times 0.5 = 0.48.$$

(b) Here, we need to calculate $P(A|G)$. Now
$$P(A|G) = \frac{P(A \cap G)}{P(G)} = \frac{P(G|A)(P(A)}{P(G)}$$
$$= \frac{0.4 \times 0.4}{0.48} = \frac{1}{3}.$$

In the above solution we have used a special case of a formula derived by the Reverend Thomas Bayes in 1763, the general version of which is as follows,

Bayes' formula

If A_1, A_2, ..., A_r are mutually exclusive and exhaustive events then for any other event B, the conditional probability of A_i (i = 1, 2, ..., r) given that B has occurred is

$$P(A_i|B) = \frac{P(B|A_i)P(A_i)}{P(B)}$$

where P(B) is as given in Rule 6.

Exercise 3.6

1. Two cards are dealt at random from an ordinary pack of playing cards.
   (a) Find the probability that the second card dealt will be an ace.
   (b) Given that the second card was an ace, find the conditional probability that the first card was also an ace.

2. Three machines, A, B and C, in a certain factory produce 50%, 25% and 25%, respectively, of the total daily output of a particular type of article. It is known that 2% of these articles produced on each of machines A and B are defective and that 3% of those produced on machine C are defective. One article is chosen at random from a day's production.
   (a) Calculate the probability that it is defective.
   (b) Given that the chosen article is defective, determine which machine was the most likely to have produced it.

3. A local football team plays equal numbers of home and away games in a season. Its probability of winning a home game is 0.75 and of winning an away game is 0.4. Given that a randomly chosen game played by this team last season was won by the team, find the conditional probability that it was an away game.

4. One box is chosen at random from three boxes labelled A, B and C, respectively. Box A contains 5 red and 5 white balls; box B contains 4 red and 6 white balls; box C contains 3 red and 7 white balls. Two balls are then drawn at random from the chosen box.
   (a) Calculate the probability that the two drawn balls will (i) both be red, (ii) be of the same colour.
   (b) Given that the two balls drawn were of the same colour, determine which box was the most likely one to have been chosen.

5. A hot-drinks vending machine supplies coffee, tea and chocolate, the demands for which are in the ratios 4:3:3. The probability that the machine is unable to supply coffee on demand is 0.02, and the corresponding probabilities for tea and chocolate are 0.03 and 0.02, respectively. Given that the machine was unable to supply a particular customer's choice, calculate the probabilities that the customer required (a) coffee, (b) tea, (c) chocolate.

6. A judicial court in a certain country may return any one of three verdicts, namely 'guilty', 'not guilty' or 'not proven'. Of the cases that have been tried by this court, 70% of the verdicts were 'guilty', 20% were 'not guilty', and 10% were 'not proven'. Suppose that when the court's verdict is 'guilty', 'not guilty' or 'not proven', the respective probabilities of the accused person being innocent are 0.05, 0.95 and 0.25. Find the conditional probability that an innocent person will be found 'guilty'.

7. A breast-screening test has probability 0.95 of giving a correct conclusion (that is, of concluding the presence of cancer in a woman who has cancer and of concluding the absence of cancer in a woman who does not have cancer). Assuming that 1% of women undergoing the test have cancer, calculate the conditional probability that a woman has cancer given that the test concluded that she does have cancer.

8. Sweets of assorted flavours are sold in tubes, each tube containing 10 sweets. The packaging process is such that 30% of the tubes contain 2 orange-flavoured sweets, 40% contain 3 orange-flavoured sweets, and 30% contain 4 orange-flavoured sweets. Three sweets were chosen at random from a randomly chosen tube and it was found that only 1 was orange-flavoured. Calculate the probability that the 7 remaining sweets in the tube include exactly 2 orange-flavoured sweets.

9. A census showed that 20% of all married couples living in a certain district had no children, 50% had one child, and 30% had two or more children. The census also showed that both the husband and wife were in employment in 70% of couples having no children, in 30% of couples having one child, and in 10% of couples having two or more children. One married couple is chosen at random.

(a) Calculate the probability that both the husband and the wife are in employment.

(b) Given that both the husband and the wife are in employment, calculate the probability that the couple have at least one child.

10. Box A contains 4 white and 6 black balls. Box B contains 3 white and 3 black balls. Two balls are drawn at random from box A and put in box B. One ball is then drawn at random from box B. Given that the ball drawn from box B is black, find the probability that the two balls transferred to B from A were both black.

11. In a multiple choice examination question, n answers are supplied, only one of which is correct. Suppose that a candidate knows the answer with probability p. If he does not know the answer, he guesses and chooses one of the answers at random. Show that if he chooses the correct answer, the probability that he actually knew the correct answer is $\dfrac{np}{1+(n-1)p}$.

12. A chest has three drawers. The first contains two gold coins, the second contains a gold and a silver coin and the third contains two silver coins. A drawer is chosen at random and from it, a coin is chosen at random. Given that the chosen coin is silver, find the probability that the other coin in the chosen drawer is gold.

3.7 Probability tree diagrams

Consider a random experiment which consists of n stages. We have already met such random experiments. For example, drawing three balls at random from a box containing balls of various colours consists of three stages, the first being the drawing of the first ball, the second the drawing of the second ball, and the third the drawing of the third ball. Let A_1 denote an event associated with the outcome of the first stage, A_2 an event associated with the outcome of the second stage, and so on. The probability that A_1 and A_2 will occur is

$$P(A_1 \cap A_2) = P(A_1)P(A_2|A_1).$$

The probability that A_1 and A_2 and A_3 will occur is

$$P(A_1 \cap A_2 \cap A_3) = P(A_1)P(A_2 \cap A_3|A_1) = P(A_1)P(A_2|A_1)P(A_3|A_1 \cap A_2).$$

This product rule extends in an obvious way for $n > 3$. The rule enables us to solve problems relating to random experiments consisting of separate stages using *probability tree diagrams*, as illustrated in the following examples.

Example 1 (Example 3 of Section 3.4)

Two cards are dealt from a shuffled pack of ordinary playing cards. Find the probability that at least one of the two cards is an ace.

Solution

The following tree diagram displays all the possible outcomes when noting whether a card is an ace or not an ace, where A denotes an ace and A′ denotes a non-ace. Along each branch we have indicated the probability of the outcome shown at the end of the branch. Thus, for example, if the first card is an ace then the second card is dealt from a pack containing 3 aces and 48 non-aces, so that the conditional probability of the second card being an ace given that the first card was an ace is 3/51.

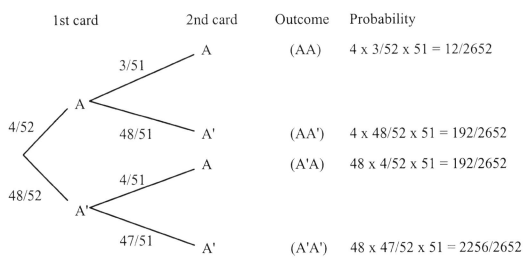

1st card   2nd card   Outcome   Probability

(AA)   4 x 3/52 x 51 = 12/2652

(AA')   4 x 48/52 x 51 = 192/2652

(A'A)   48 x 4/52 x 51 = 192/2652

(A'A')   48 x 47/52 x 51 = 2256/2652

[Note that in a probability tree diagram the probabilities of all the branches from one point must add to unity, and the probabilities of all the ordered outcomes must also add to unity; these should be checked after the diagram has been drawn].

At least one ace is dealt if the outcome is (AA) or (AA') or (A'A). Since these are mutually exclusive

$$P(\text{at least one ace}) = P(AA) + P(AA') + P(A'A)$$
$$= (12 + 192 + 192)/2652 = 396/2652 = 33/221.$$

[Alternatively, since the complement of "at least one ace" is "no ace", we have

$$P(\text{at least one ace}) = 1 - P(\text{no ace}) = 1 - P(A'A')$$
$$= 1 - 2256/2652 = 33/221].$$

Example 2 (Part of Example 7 of Section 3.4)

A box contains 5 red, 7 blue and 8 white balls. Three balls are drawn at random (without replacement) from this box. Calculate the probability that the drawn balls will be such that (a) two are red and one is blue, (b) all three are of the same colour. (c) Given that the drawn balls are of the same colour, find the probability that they are red.

Solution

This is a 3-stage experiment and there are three possible outcomes at each stage (red, blue and white), which means that there will be a total of $3 \times 3 \times 3 = 27$ ordered outcomes. The probability tree diagram will be large in order to cover all these possibilities. This can be avoided by restricting consideration to only those branches which lead to the event of interest.

(a) The event "2 are red and one is blue" will occur only if the ordered outcome is one of (RRB), (RBR), (BRR), where R denotes a red ball and B denotes a blue ball. The corresponding branches of the probability tree diagram are shown below.

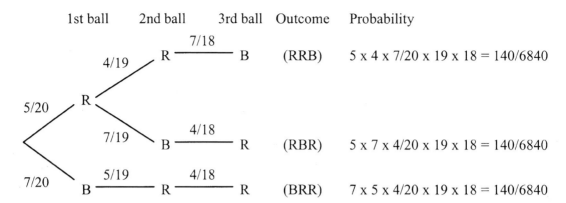

It follows that

$$P(2 \text{ red and } 1 \text{ blue}) = 3 \times 140/6840 = 420/6840 = 7/114.$$

(b) The event "all 3 are of the same colour" will occur only if the ordered outcome is one of (RRR), (BBB), (WWW), where W denotes a white ball. The required branches of the probability tree diagram are as follows.

1st ball	2nd ball	3rd ball	Outcome	Probability
5/20 R — 4/19 — R — 3/18 — R			(RRR)	5 x 4 x 3/20 x 19 x 18 = 60/6840
7/20 B — 6/19 — B — 5/18 — B			(BBB)	7 x 6 x 5/20 x 19 x 18 = 210/6840
8/20 W — 7/19 — W — 6/18 — W			(WWW)	8 x 7 x 6/20 x 19 x 18 = 336/6840

Therefore,

$$P(\text{all the same colour}) = (60 + 210 + 336)/6840 = 101/1140.$$

(c) We can use Bayes' formula to find the probability that all three balls are red, given that they are all of the same colour, as follows.

$$P(RRR \mid \text{All 3 same colour}) = \frac{P(RRR)}{P(RRR) + P(BBB) + P(WWW)}$$

$$= \frac{60\!\!\not{}6840}{60\!\!\not{}6840 + 210\!\!\not{}6840 + 336\!\!\not{}6840}$$

$$= 10\!\!\not{}101 \, .$$

Many of the examples and exercises in Sections 3.4 and 3.6 can be answered using probability tree diagrams, a method that may be preferred by some.

Exercise 3.7

1. Three valves are drawn at random from a box containing three faulty and seven good valves. (a) Find the probability that at least one good valve will be drawn. (b) Given that the first valve drawn was a good one, find the conditional probability that all three drawn were good.

2. A mouse placed in laboratory T-maze has the choice of turning left for food or turning right and receiving a mild electric shock. On its first run, a mouse is just as likely to turn left as it is to turn right. On any subsequent run, the probability that the mouse will turn left is (i) 0.6 if it received food on the preceding run, and (ii) 0.8 if it received a shock on the preceding run. By drawing a probability tree diagram, or otherwise, find the probability that

(a) the mouse will turn left on its second run,

(b) the mouse will turn left on its third run.

3. Find the probability that the first three cards dealt from a shuffled pack of ordinary cards will be (a) three spades, (b) two spades and one heart, (c) of three different suits.

4. A fair cubical die is tossed. If the score obtained is a multiple of 3, one ball is drawn at random from a box containing 5 red, 3 white and 8 blue balls. If the score obtained is not a multiple of 3, one ball is drawn at random from a box containing 3 red and 5 white balls.

(a) Find the probability that a red ball will be drawn.

(b) Given that the drawn ball was white, find the probability that the score obtained on the die was (i) a multiple of 3, (ii) 5.

5. Bag A contains 4 white balls and 3 red balls, and bag B contains 2 white balls and 5 red balls. A biased coin is such that when tossed the probability of a head is $\frac{2}{3}$. This coin is

tossed; if a head is obtained, one ball is drawn at random from bag A, otherwise one ball is drawn at random from bag B.

(a)   Calculate the probability that a red ball will be drawn.

(b)   Given that a red ball is drawn, find the probability that it came from bag A.

6.   Anwen, Bethan and Carys share a flat. On any day the probability that Anwen cooks the evening meal is 0.5, the probability that Bethan cooks it is 0.3 and the probability that Carys cooks it is 0.2. The probability that an evening meal turns out to be unsatisfactory is 0.02 when Anwen cooks it, 0.03 when Bethan cooks it and 0.04 when Carys cooks it.

(a)   Find the probability that an evening meal will turn out to be unsatisfactory.

(b)   Given that an evening meal was satisfactory, find the probability that Bethan cooked it.

7.   Alec and Bill play a game which consists of two stages. In the first stage two fair dice are thrown. In the second stage one of the boys draws a card at random from a pack of 10 cards numbered from 1 to 10. Alex will draw the card if the sum of the scores on the two dice is 6 or less, otherwise Bill will draw the card. If the boy drawing the card draws one which is numbered 1 or 2, that boy wins the game; otherwise, the other boy wins the game.

(a)   Show that Alec's probability of winning the game is 0.55.

(b)   Given that a game is won by Alec, find the probability that it was Alec who drew the card.

3.8   Independent events and independent experiments

Definition. Two events are said to be *independent* if the probability of either occurring is unaffected by the knowledge that the other has occurred.

Symbolically, two events A and B are independent if

$$P(A \mid B) = P(A). \tag{1}$$

On using (1) we see that

$$P(B \mid A) = \frac{P(A \cap B)}{P(A)} = \frac{P(A|B)\, P(B)}{P(A)} = P(B). \tag{2}$$

Combining (1) and (2) it follows that two events A and B are independent if

$$P(A \cap B) = P(A \mid B)P(B) = P(A)P(B), \tag{3}$$

which is a more useful form in practice.

The converse is also true. That is, if A and B are independent then (1), (2) and (3) are true.

We have already met several examples in Sections 3.5 and 3.6 of events that are not independent. For instance, consider Example 1 of Section 3.6 in which two balls are drawn at random from a box containing 12 red balls and 8 blue balls. Let A denote the event that the first ball drawn is blue and let B denote the event that the second ball drawn is blue. We showed that

$$P(B\,|\,A) = \frac{7}{19} \text{ but } P(B) = \frac{8}{20} ,$$

so that A and B are not independent.

We now show that if A and B are independent, then A and B' are also independent.

Using Rule 4

$$
\begin{aligned}
P(A\cap B') &= P(A) - P(A\cap B) \\
&= P(A) - P(A)P(B) \text{ by (3) above} \\
&= P(A)[1 - P(B)] = P(A)P(B') ,
\end{aligned}
$$

which establishes that A and B' are also independent. In addition, A' and B are independent, and A' and B' are independent, results which you are asked to verify in Question 4 of the following exercise.

Example 1

The two events A and B are independent and such that $P(A) = 0.2$ and $P(A\cup B) = 0.4$. Evaluate (a) P(B) and (b) $P(A'\cap B)$.

Solution

(a)   By Rule 3

$$
\begin{aligned}
P(A\cup B) &= P(A) + P(B) - P(A\cap B) \\
&= P(A) + P(B) - P(A)P(B), \text{ on using (3).}
\end{aligned}
$$

Substituting the given probabilities we have

$$0.4 = 0.2 + P(B) - 0.2P(B),$$

or $0.8P(B) = 0.2,$

from which it follows that $P(B) = 0.25$.

(b) Since A and B are independent, A' and B are also independent. Therefore

$$
\begin{aligned}
P(A'\cap B) &= P(A')P(B) \\
&= (1 - 0.2) \times 0.25 = 0.2.
\end{aligned}
$$

Example 2

A fair coin is tossed three times. Let A denote the event that three heads or three tails are tossed, B the event that at least two heads are tossed, and C the event that at most two heads are tossed. Show that (a) A and B are independent, (b) A and C are not independent.

Solution

There are 8 possible ordered outcomes for the three tosses, namely

(HHH), (HHT), (HTH), (THH), (HTT), (THT), (TTH), (TTT)

and these are equally probable.

A = 3 heads or 3 tails = {(HHH), (TTT)}

B = at least 2 heads = {(HHH), (HHT), (HTH), (THH)}

C = at most 2 heads = {(HHT), (HTH), (THH), (HTT), (THT), (TTH), (TTT)}.

We have

A∩B = {(HHH)}, A∩C = {(TTT)}.

(a) $P(A \cap B) = \frac{1}{8}$, $P(A) = \frac{2}{8}$, $P(B) = \frac{4}{8}$.

Since P(A∩B) = P(A)P(B) = 1/8, it follows that A and B are independent.

(b) $P(A \cap C) = \frac{1}{8}$, $P(A) = \frac{2}{8}$, $P(C) = \frac{7}{8}$.

Since P(A∩C) ≠ P(A)P(C), A and C are not independent.

Exercise 3.8a

1.   Given that A and B are independent events such that P(A) = 0.5 and P(B) = 0.4, evaluate (a) P(A∩B), (b) P(A∪B).

2.   Given that A and B are two events such that P(A) = 0.6, P(B′) = 0.7, and P(A∪B) = 0.72, show that A and B are independent.

3.   Two events A and B are such that P(A) = 0.3, P(B|A) = 0.2 and P(A∪B) = 0.44. Show that A and B are independent.

4.   Given that A and B are independent, show that (a) A′ and B are independent, (b) A′ and B′ are independent.

5.   The independent events A, B are such that
$$P(A \cup B) = 0.44; \ P(A \cap B) = 0.06.$$
Find the possible values of P(A) and P(B).

6.   One card is drawn at random from an ordinary pack of playing cards. Let A denote the event that the chosen card is a heart and let B denote the event that it is an honour card (ace, king, queen or jack). Show that A and B are independent.

7.   A fair red cubical die and a fair blue cubical die are thrown together. Let A denote the event that the score on the red die is 1 and let B denote the event that the sum of the two scores is 7. Determine whether or not A and B are independent.

8.   Let A denote the event that a family has children of both sexes, and B the event that a family has at most one girl. It may be assumed that all possible sex distributions of a family's children ordered by age are equally probable. Show that (a) A and B are

independent if a family has 3 children, (b) A and B are not independent if a family has 2 children.

9. Two cards are dealt from an ordinary pack of playing cards. Let A denote the event that the first card is a spade, B the event that the second card is a king, and C the event that the first card is either an ace or a king. Determine which pairs of A, B and C are independent.

10. A class contains 20 pupils. Of these, 15 study Mathematics and 8 study Science. A pupil is selected at random. Let M denote the event that the chosen pupil studies Mathematics and let S denote the event that the chosen pupil studies Science.

(a) Given that 5 pupils in the class study both Mathematics and Science, show that M and S are not independent.

(b) Given that x pupils in the class study both Mathematics and Science and that M and S are independent, find the value of x.

Independent random experiments

Definition. Two or more random experiments are said to be *independent* if they are performed in such a way that the probabilities of the possible outcomes of any one of them are the same whatever the outcomes of the others.

Some examples of independent random experiments are:

(1) Throwing a die and a coin.

(2) Tossing a coin several times.

(3) Drawing objects at random *with replacement* from a collection of objects.

Consider two independent random experiments. Let A_1 and A_2 denote events with respect to the first and second experiment, respectively. It is clear that A_1 and A_2 are independent events so that $P(A_1 \cap A_2) = P(A_1)P(A_2)$. Extending this result to k independent random experiments, if A_i is an event associated with the ith experiment (i = 1, 2, 3, ..., k), then

$$P(A_1 \cap A_2 \cap A_3 \cap \ldots \cap A_k) = P(A_1) \times P(A_2) \times P(A_3) \times \ldots \times P(A_k),$$

which is a special form of the product rule in Section 3.7.

Example 3

A fair cubical die is thrown four times. Calculate the probability that (a) each throw gives an even score, (b) at least one 6 is thrown.

Solution

The four throws are four independent experiments each of which is the throwing of the die once.

(a)   Let A_1, A_2, A_3 and A_4 denote the events that the first, second, third and fourth throws give an even score. Since the probability of an even score in one throw of a fair die is ½, $P(A_1) = P(A_2) = P(A_3) = P(A_4) = ½$. Since the throws are independent,

$$P(A_1 \cap A_2 \cap A_3 \cap A_4) = P(A_1) \times P(A_2) \times P(A_3) \times P(A_4) = \left(\frac{1}{2}\right)^4 = \frac{1}{16}$$

(b)   To find the probability that at least one 6 is thrown we could find the probabilities of throwing one, two, three and four 6s and then add them (since they are mutually exclusive). However, it is easier to find the probability of the complementary event that no 6 is thrown. Let B_1, B_2, B_3, and B_4 denote the events that the first, second, third and fourth throws do not give a 6. Each of these has probability 5/6 and the probability of no 6 being thrown is

$$P(B_1 \cap B_2 \cap B_3 \cap B_4) = P(B_1) \times P(B_2) \times P(B_3) \times P(B_4) = \left(\frac{5}{6}\right)^4 = \frac{625}{1296}$$

Hence, the probability of at least one 6 is $1 - \dfrac{625}{1296} = \dfrac{671}{1296}$.

Example 4

A father and son are at a shooting range. Independently for each shot fired by the father the probability that it will hit the target is 0.8, and for the son the corresponding probability is 0.4.

(a)   If each of them fires two shots at the target find the probability that all four shots hit the target.

(b)   If the son is only allowed to have two shots at the target, find the smallest number of shots that the father should have in order that the probability of one or more of the shots hitting the target is at least 0.99.

Solution

(a)   Let F_1 and F_2 denote the events that the father's first and second shot, respectively, hits the target. Let S_1 and S_2 denote the events that the son's first and second shot, respectively, hits the target. Since these four events are independent, the probability that all four shots hit the target is

$$P(F_1 \cap F_2 \cap S_1 \cap S_2) = P(F_1) \times P(F_2) \times P(S_1) \times P(S_2)$$
$$= 0.8 \times 0.8 \times 0.4 \times 0.4 = 0.1024.$$

(b)   Suppose that the father is allowed n shots at the target. Let E denote the event that in the $(n + 2)$ shots the target will be hit one or more times, so that E' is the event that all $(n + 2)$ shots miss the target.

Extending the notation in (a) we have

$$P(E') = P(S_1' \cap S_2' \cap F_1' \cap F_2' \cap \ldots \cap F_n')$$
$$= P(S_1') \times P(S_2') \times P(F_1') \times P(F_2') \times \ldots \times P(F_n')$$
$$= 0.6^2 \times 0.2^n = 0.36 \times 0.2^n$$

Thus, $P(E) = 1 - 0.36 \times 0.2^n$.

We want to find the smallest n for which

$$1 - 0.36 \times 0.2^n \geq 0.99,$$

or equivalently

$$0.2^n \leq 0.01/0.36$$

Taking logarithms we find that

$$n \geq \frac{\ln(0.01/0.36)}{\ln 0.2} = 2.23,$$

the reversal of the inequality sign being due to the fact that we have divided by a negative number ($\ln 0.2$).

It follows that the father should be allowed at least 3 shots in order that there is a probability of at least 0.99 that the target will be hit.

Exercise 3.8b

1. The probability that Jane can solve a certain problem is 0.4 and that Alice can solve it is 0.3. If they both try independently, find the probability that the problem is solved by at least one of the two girls.

2. A fair die is thrown and a card is drawn at random from an ordinary pack of playing cards. Find the probability that (a) the score thrown is even and the drawn card is red, (b) the score thrown is even *or* the drawn card is red.

3. A mechanism consists of three components and will operate properly only if all three components are functioning. Assuming that the three components function independently and have probabilities 0.02, 0.05, and 0.1, respectively, of developing a fault, find the probability that the mechanism will not operate properly. Given that the mechanism is not operating properly, find the probability that it is because exactly one of the components has developed a fault.

4. Three men at a shooting range have probabilities of 0.17, 0.25 and 0.33 of hitting the 'bull' with a single shot. (a) Each man fires one shot. (i) Calculate the probability that exactly one of the three shots hits the 'bull'. (ii) Given that only one shot hit the 'bull', find the probability that it was fired by the man who had the least probability of hitting the 'bull'. (b) For each of the men, find the least number of shots he should fire to ensure a probability of at least 0.9 that one or more of his shots will hit the 'bull'.

5. Independently, three brothers speak the truth with probabilities 0.9, 0.8 and 0.7, respectively. One day each was asked who had been responsible for a certain misdemeanour. Find the probabilities that (a) all three will answer truthfully, (b) only two of them will answer truthfully.

6. A girl plays a series of three games in each of which her probabilities of winning, drawing and losing are 0.5, 0.25 and 0.25, respectively. Find the probability that she will win more games than she will lose.

7. Two children, Ann and Brian, throw a die alternately and the first to throw a '6' is the winner. Given that Ann throws first, calculate the probability that Brian wins

(a) on his 1st throw,

(b) on his 2nd throw,

(c) on his nth throw.

Use (c) to calculate the probability that Brian wins the game.

3.9 Probability rules summarised

Listed below are the various rules of probability introduced in this chapter.

1. $P(A') = 1 - P(A)$.

2. If A, B, C, ... are mutually exclusive events then

$$P(A \cup B \cup C \cup \ldots) = P(A) + P(B) + P(C) + \ldots$$

3. For any two events A and B

(a) $P(A \cup B) = P(A) + P(B) - P(A \cap B)$,

(b) $P(A \cap B') = P(A) - P(A \cap B)$,

(c) $P(A' \cap B') = 1 - P(A \cup B)$; $P(A' \cup B') = 1 - P(A \cap B)$,

(d) $P(A \cap B) = P(A \mid B)P(B) = P(B \mid A)P(A)$.

4. If $A_1, A_2, \ldots A_k$ are mutually exclusive and exhaustive events, then for any other event B

(a) $P(B) = P(B \mid A_1)P(A_1) + P(B \mid A_2)P(A_2) + \ldots + P(B \mid A_k)P(A_k)$

(b) $P(A_i \mid B) = \dfrac{P(B \mid A_i)P(A_i)}{P(B)}$ for any i = 1, 2, ... k.

5. If $A_1, A_2, \ldots A_k$, respectively, are k events associated with k different stages of a random experiment, or with k different random experiments then

$$P(A_1 \cap A_2 \cap \ldots \cap A_k) = P(A_1) \, P(A_2 \mid A_1)P(A_3 \mid A_1 \cap A_2) \ldots P(A_k \mid A_1 \cap A_2 \cap \ldots \cap A_{k-1})$$

6. If $A_1, A_2, \ldots A_k$ are k independent events then

$$P(A_1 \cap A_2 \cap \ldots \cap A_k) = P(A_1)P(A_2) \ldots P(A_k).$$

Miscellaneous Questions on Chapter 3

1. (1987) The two events A and B are such that $P(A) = 0.2$, $P(B) = 0.3$, and $P(A \cup B) = 0.4$.

(i) Determine whether or not A and B are independent.

(ii) Evaluate $P(B \mid A')$. [4]

2. (1987) A pack of 52 playing cards consists of 4 aces, 12 picture cards, and 36 other cards. A hand of 13 cards is dealt at random without replacement from the pack.

(i) Write down expressions, but **do not** simplify them, for the probabilities that the hand will include (a) exactly 2 aces and 11 picture cards, (b) exactly 2 aces and exactly 8 picture cards.

(ii) Let p_1 denote the probability that the hand will include no ace and exactly 8 picture cards, and let p_2 denote the probability that the hand will include exactly 3 aces and exactly 6 picture cards. Show that $p_1/p_2 = 6/7$. [6]

3. (1987) A box contains ten coins. Four of the coins are fair, while each of the other six coins is such that when tossed the probability of obtaining a head is $\frac{1}{4}$.

(i) One coin is chosen at random from the box and is tossed twice. Let A denote the event that the first toss gives a head, and let B denote the event that the second toss gives a head. Show that A and B are not independent. [7]

(ii) Suppose, instead, that two coins are chosen at random from the ten coins in the box and that they are tossed together once.

(a) Calculate the probability that one head and one tail will be obtained.

(b) Given that one head and one tail were obtained, calculate the conditional probability that at least one of the two chosen coins was a fair coin. [8]

4. (1988) The two events A and B are such that $P(A) = 0.2$, $P(B) = 0.4$, and $P(A|B) = 0.3$.

    (i) State, with your reason, whether A and B are independent. [1]

    (ii) Find the values of $P(A \cup B)$ and $P(B|A)$. [3]

5. (1989) Three cards are to be drawn at random without replacement from a pack of ten cards. Six of the cards in the pack are red and numbered from 1 to 6, respectively, while the other four cards are blue and numbered from 1 to 4, respectively. Calculate the probabilities that (i) exactly two red cards will be drawn, (ii) exactly one 2 will be drawn. [4]

6. (1989) (a) A committee of 9 persons is to be selected from a group of 13 persons, of whom 7 are males and 6 are females. Calculate the probability that more females than males will be selected in each of the cases when

(i)   the selection is made randomly,

(ii) the selection is made randomly subject to there being at least 4 females on the committee. [7]

(b)   The three events A, B and C are such that

$$P(A) = \frac{1}{5}, \ P(B) = \frac{1}{10}, \ P(A \cup C) = \frac{7}{15}, \ P(B \cup C) = \frac{23}{60},$$

and the events A and C are independent.

(i)   Show that $P(C) = 1/3$.

(ii) Determine whether or not B and C are independent.

(iii) Given further that A and B are mutually exclusive, evaluate $P(A \cup B | C)$. [8]

7.   (1990)   Two events A and B are such that $P(A) = 0.5$, $P(B) = 0.3$, and $P(A \cap B) = 0.1$. Calculate (i) $P(A \cup B)$, (ii) $P(A' \cap B)$, (iii) the probability that exactly one of the two events occurs. [5]

8.   (1990) A bag contains nine balls of which four are red, three are blue, and two are white. Three of these balls are to be selected at random without replacement.

(i)   Calculate the probability that one ball of each colour will be selected.

(ii) Calculate the probability that the three balls selected will be of the same colour.

(iii) Given that the three selected balls were not all of the same colour, calculate the conditional probability that two of the selected balls were red. [7]

9.   (1990) Two machines, A and B, are used to produce identical items. Independently for each item produced on machine A, the probability that it is defective is 0.01, while for an item produced on machine B the corresponding probability is 0.03.

Of the total output of items produced in a day, 60% are produced on machine A and 40% are produced on machine B.

(i)   If one item is chosen at random from a day's output, show that the probability of it being nondefective is 0.982.

(ii) Two items are chosen at random from a day's output and both are found to be nondefective. Calculate, correct to three decimal places, the conditional probability that one of the items was produced on machine A and the other was produced on machine B. [7]

10.   (1991)   Two events A and B are such that $P(A) = 0.6$, $P(A \cap B) = 0.2$ and $P(A \cup B) = 0.7$. Calculate (i) $P(B)$, (ii) $P(B'|A)$. [3]

11.   (1991) An insurance company offering comprehensive policies to car drivers classifies each applicant as being high-risk, average-risk, or low-risk. Independently for each year, the probability that a high-risk driver will submit a claim is 0.4; the corresponding probabilities for an average-risk driver and a low-risk driver are 0.2 and 0.1,

respectively. The proportions of the policy holders who have been classified as high-risk, average-risk, and low-risk are 0.3, 0.6 and 0.1, respectively.

(i) Calculate the probability that a randomly chosen policy holder will submit a claim in a year.

(ii) Given that a randomly chosen policy holder did make a claim in one year, calculate the conditional probability that the policy holder was a high-risk driver.

(iii) Calculate the conditional probability that a policy holder chosen at random from those who made a claim in one year will also make a claim the following year. [8]

12. (1992) A box contains 10 videos of which 6 are films and 4 are educational. If 4 of these videos are chosen at random, calculate the probabilities that (i) all four will be films, (ii) two will be films and the other two educational. [3]

13. (1992) A factory has three machines A, B and C producing a particular type of item. In a day's output, 50% of the items are produced on A, 30% on B and 20% on C. A randomly chosen item from those produced on A has probability 0.01 of being defective, the corresponding probabilities for items produced on B and C being 0.02 and 0.03 respectively.

(i) If an item is chosen at random from a day's output, calculate the probability that it will be defective.

(ii) Given that two items chosen at random from a day's output were produced on the same machine and were both defective, calculate the conditional probability that both items were produced on machine A. [5]

14. (1993) A and B are independent events associated with a random experiment and are such that in any trial of the experiment the probability that A will occur is 0.8 and the probability that B will occur is 0.5.

(a) Find the probability that in one trial of the experiment both A and B will occur.

(b) Find the probability that in one trial of the experiment at least one of A and B will occur. [3]

15. (1994) Two unbiased dice are thrown simultaneously. Calculate the probability that

(i) the scores on both dice are at least 3,

(ii) the scores on the two dice differ by 2. [4]

16. (1994) A box contains 4 red balls and 2 blue balls. A random sample of 3 balls is selected from the box. Calculate the probability that 2 red balls and 1 blue ball are selected, given that the selection is made (i) without replacement, (ii) with replacement. [4]

17. (1994) It is known that 1% of the population suffer from a certain disease. A diagnostic test for the disease gives a positive response with probability 0.98 if the disease is present. If the disease is not present, the probability of a positive response is 0.005.

(a) A test is applied to a randomly selected member of the population.

(i) Show that the probability of obtaining a positive response is 0.01475.

(ii) Given that a positive response is obtained, calculate the probability that the person has the disease.

(b) A randomly selected person is tested and responds positively. This person is tested again. Calculate the probability that this second test is positive. [7]

18. (1994) Three events A, B C are such that

$$P(B) = \frac{1}{4}, \ P(C) = \frac{1}{3}, \ P(A \cup B) = \frac{3}{5}, \ P(A \cup C) = \frac{2}{3}.$$

The events A, B are independent and the events B, C are mutually exclusive.

(i) Find P(A).

(ii) Determine whether or not A, C are independent.

(iii) Show that $P(B \cup C | A) = \frac{15}{28}$. [8]

19. (1995) A committee consists of 6 men and 4 women. A sub-committee of 4 members is to be formed and it is decided to select these 4 members at random. Find the probability that the sub-committee contains at least one member of each sex. [4]

20. (1995) The events A, B are independent. Given that P(A) = 0.2 and P(A∪B) = 0.5, calculate (a) P(B), (b) P(A'∩B'), (c) P(A|A∪B). [5]

21. (S1 Jan 1996) Two events A, B are such that P(A) = 0.4, P(B) = 0.5, P(A∪B) = 0.6.

(a) Determine whether or not A, B are independent.

(b) Evaluate P(B|A'). [5]

22. (S1 Jan 1996) A diagnostic test is used to detect a certain disease which is known to afflict 3% of the population. When applied to a person with the disease, it gives a positive response with probability 0.95; when applied to a person who does not have the disease, it gives a positive response with probability 0.01. The test is applied to a randomly chosen member of the population.

(a) Calculate the probability that a positive response is obtained.

(b) Given that a positive response is obtained, calculate the probability that the person has the disease. [5]

23. (S1 June 1996) Two independent events A and B are such that

P(A) = x; P(B) = y; P(A∪B) = 0.58; P(A∩B) = 0.12.

(a) Write down two equations connecting x and y.

(b) Given that A is more likely to occur than B, find the value of x. [4]

24. (A3 1996) A and B are independent events associated with a random experiment. The probabilities of A, B occurring in a single trial of the experiment are given by

P(A) = 0.3; P(B) = 0.4.

(a) Find the probability that

(i) both A and B occur in a single trial,

(ii) exactly one of A or B occurs in a single trial. [3]

25. (A3 June 1996) A football club introduces a new weekly lottery. Supporters buy cards on which they mark four different numbers chosen from the integers 1, 2, 3,..., 20. Every Saturday evening, a draw is held in which four balls are chosen at random, without replacement, from twenty balls numbered 1, 2, 3, . . ., 20, respectively. The winning numbers are the numbers on the four chosen balls. Calculate the probability that a supporter who buys one card marks

(a) 4 winning numbers   (b) 2 winning numbers, in a particular week. [5]

**COLEG GWENT
PONTYPOOL CAMPUS
BLAENDARE ROAD
PONTYPOOL
NP4 5YE**

Chapter 4

Discrete Random Variables

4.1 Random variables

Definition. A *random variable* is a verbal description of a rule for assigning a numerical value to every outcome of a random experiment. A random variable will be denoted by a capital letter close to the end of the alphabet (e.g. W, X, Y, Z), and an arbitrary observed value will be denoted by the corresponding lower case letter (e.g. w, x, y, z).

Example 1

Consider the random experiment in which a coin is tossed three times. The sample space, in an obvious notation, is

$$S = \{(HHH), (HHT), (HTH), (THH), (HTT), (THT), (TTH), (TTT)\}.$$

Two possible random variables to associate with this experiment are:

(1)   X = the number of heads tossed, the possible values for which are $x = 0, 1, 2, 3$.
(2)   Y = the difference between the number of heads and number of tails tossed, having
        possible values $y = 1, 3$.

Example 2

Consider the random experiment in which a coin is tossed until a head is obtained.
Let Z = the number of tosses made. Then Z has the possible values $z = 1, 2, 3, 4, \ldots$.

Example 3

Consider the random experiment in which a hand of 13 cards is dealt from an ordinary pack of playing cards. Two possible random variables in this case are

(1)   X = the number of red cards dealt, having possible values x = 0, 1, 2, 3, ..., 13.

(2)   Y = the number of aces dealt, having possible values y = 0, 1, 2, 3, 4.

In each of the above examples the possible values of the random variable can be listed individually. Such a random variable is said to be *discrete* and this chapter will be restricted to discrete random variables. (Random variables whose possible values cannot be listed individually will be considered in the next chapter).

Exercise 4.1

Write down all the possible values of each of the following random variables.

1.   The number of heads when a coin is tossed twice.

2.   The number of boys in a family having four children.

3.   The number of court cards (king, queen or jack) in a hand of 13 cards dealt from an ordinary pack of playing cards.

4.   The highest score when a cubical die is thrown three times.

5.   The number of incoming telephone calls to a school during a week.

6.   The number of times a cubical die is thrown until a score of 6 is obtained.

4.2   Distribution of a discrete random variable

Having listed the possible values of a random variable, the next step is to determine their probabilities of occurring. When doing so, always check that the probabilities sum to unity (since one of the listed values must occur). If x is a possible value of the random variable X, we write $P(X = x)$ for the probability that the observed value of X will be x. A specification of all possible values of X and their corresponding probabilities is referred to as the *distribution* of X. (More strictly, it is the *probability distribution* of X since one unit of probability is distributed over all the possible values of X).

Example 1

A fair coin is tossed three times. Find the distribution of the number of heads tossed.

Solution

The sample space for the outcomes of the three tosses is

$$S = \{(HHH), (HHT), (HTH), (THH), (HTT), (THT), (TTH), (TTT)\}$$

and since the coin is fair, these 8 outcomes are equally probable.

Let X denote the number of heads tossed, the possible values of which are x = 0, 1, 2, 3. X = 0 occurs if no head is tossed; that is, if the outcome is (TTT). It follows that P(X = 0) = 1/8.

X = 1 occurs if one head is tossed; that is if the outcome is one of (HTT), (THT) or (TTH), so that P(X = 1) = 3/8.

Similarly, we find that P(X = 2) = 3/8 and P(X = 3) = 1/8.

The distribution of X in this case can be displayed tabularly as follows.

x	0	1	2	3
P(X = x)	$\dfrac{1}{8}$	$\dfrac{3}{8}$	$\dfrac{3}{8}$	$\dfrac{1}{8}$

Observe that the probabilities do sum to 1 as required.

Example 2

Four balls are drawn without replacement from a bag containing 7 red balls and 6 blue balls. Find the distribution of the number of red balls drawn.

Solution

Let X denote the number of red balls drawn. The possible values of X are x = 0, 1, 2, 3, 4.

$$P(X = 0) = P(4 \text{ blue balls}) = \binom{6}{4} \Big/ \binom{13}{4} = \frac{15}{715} = \frac{3}{143},$$

$$P(X = 1) = P(3 \text{ blue balls and 1 red ball}) = \binom{6}{3} \times \binom{7}{1} \Big/ \binom{13}{4} = \frac{140}{715} = \frac{28}{143},$$

$$P(X = 2) = P(2 \text{ blue balls and 2 red balls}) = \binom{6}{2} \times \binom{7}{2} \Big/ \binom{13}{4} = \frac{315}{715} = \frac{63}{143}$$

$$P(X = 3) = P(1 \text{ blue ball and 3 red balls}) = \binom{6}{1} \times \binom{7}{3} \Big/ \binom{13}{4} = \frac{210}{715} = \frac{42}{143}$$

$$P(X = 4) = P(4 \text{ red balls}) = \binom{7}{4} \Big/ \binom{13}{4} = \frac{35}{715} = \frac{7}{143}.$$

The distribution of X is as shown in the following table.

x	0	1	2	3	4
P(X = x)	$\dfrac{3}{143}$	$\dfrac{28}{143}$	$\dfrac{63}{143}$	$\dfrac{42}{143}$	$\dfrac{7}{143}$

(As a check we see that the probabilities do sum to unity). Observe that since $X = 2$ has the highest probability of occurring, the most likely number of red balls that will be drawn is 2.

An alternative method for answering Example 2, which does not require the formal use of combinations is one which considers ordered outcomes. The event $X = 0$ will occur only if the sequence of colours drawn is BBBB, where B denotes a blue ball. Using the product rule for probabilities we have

$$P(X = 0) = \frac{6}{13} \times \frac{5}{12} \times \frac{4}{11} \times \frac{3}{10} = \frac{3}{143}.$$

The event $X = 1$ will occur if the sequence of colours is any one of BBBR, BBRB, BRBB, RBBB, where R denotes a red ball. The probability of the sequence BBBR is

$$\frac{6}{13} \times \frac{5}{12} \times \frac{4}{11} \times \frac{7}{10} = \frac{7}{143}.$$

It is easily verified that each of the other three sequences also has this probability of occurring (the only difference will be the order in which the numerators appear). Thus

$$P(X = 1) = 4 \times \frac{7}{143} = \frac{28}{143}.$$

It is left as an exercise to show that this method gives the values of $P(X = 2)$, $P(X = 3)$ and $P(X = 4)$ shown in the above table.

Example 3

Find the distribution of the number of times a fair die has to be thrown if throwing stops when a multiple of 3 occurs.

Solution

Let Y denote the number of times the die is thrown until a multiple of 3 occurs. The possible values of Y are $y = 1, 2, 3, 4, \ldots$. Since we do not know what the greatest value of Y will be, it is not feasible to evaluate $P(Y = y)$ for each possible value of Y. Instead, we try to find a general expression for $P(Y = y)$, where y is an arbitrary value of Y.

Now, $Y = y$ will occur if each of the first $(y - 1)$ throws gives a score which is not a multiple of 3 and the yth throw gives a score which is a multiple of 3. Since the throws are independent and in each throw the probability of getting a score which is a multiple of 3 (i.e. 3 or 6) is 1/3, it follows that

$$P(Y = y) = \left(\frac{2}{3}\right)^{y-1} \times \frac{1}{3}, \text{ for } y = 1, 2, 3, 4, \ldots.$$

It may be verified that the sum of these probabilities is unity on using the formula for the sum of an infinite geometric series having first term $a = 1/3$ and common ratio $r = 2/3$.

Exercise 4.2

1. A fair cubical die is to be thrown twice. Find the distribution of the number of 6's that will be obtained,

2. Three balls are drawn at random without replacement from a box containing 3 white balls and 9 black balls. Find the distribution of the number of white balls that will be drawn.

3. The probability that a mass produced item will be defective is 0.01. Find the distribution of the number of defectives in a random sample of two of the items.

4. A bag contains 24 balls of which 5 are red. A random sample of 3 balls is drawn from the bag one after the other. Find the distribution of the number of red balls that are drawn in each of the cases when

(a) the sampling is without replacement,

(b) the sampling is with replacement.

5. The discrete random variable X has the distribution shown in the following table. Find the value of α.

x	0	1	2	3
P(X = x)	α	α^2	$\alpha^2 + \alpha$	$3\alpha^2 + 2\alpha$

6. Three balls are drawn at random without replacement from a box containing 6 red, 3 white and 2 blue balls. Each red ball drawn scores 2 points, each white ball drawn scores 3 points and each blue ball drawn scores 5 points. Find the distribution of the sum of the three scores.

7. A biased coin is such that when tossed, the probability of a head is 0.4. The coin is to be tossed until a head is obtained. Find the distribution of the number of tosses that will be made.

8. There are five envelopes in a box. Each of three of the envelopes contains 3 red discs and 1 white disc, while each of the other two envelopes contains 2 red discs and 2 white discs. Two of the envelopes are chosen at random and one disc is drawn at random from each of the chosen envelopes. Find the distribution of the number of red discs that are drawn.

9. In an investigation of animal behaviour, a mouse has to choose between four similar doors. One door leads to food while each of the other doors will give the mouse a mild electric shock. If the mouse chooses a door which gives it an electric shock it is returned to the starting point to have another attempt. This continues until the mouse chooses the door leading to food, or until it has had a total of four attempts, whichever occurs first.

Let X denote the number of attempts by the mouse. Find the distribution of X in each of the following cases.

(a)   The mouse is equally likely to choose any one of the four doors at each attempt.

(b)   At each attempt the mouse is equally likely to choose any one of the doors that have not already been chosen.

(c)   The mouse never chooses the same door on two successive attempts, but otherwise chooses a door at random.

4.3 Expected value

Consider a discrete random variable X associated with a particular random experiment. Denote the possible values of X by $x = x_1, x_2, \ldots, x_k$. Suppose that in n independent trials of the experiment, X is observed to take the value x_1 in n_1 of the trials, the value x_2 in n_2 of the trials, $\ldots$, and the value x_k in n_k of the trials, where $n_1 + n_2 + \ldots + n_k = n$.

The *average* or *mean* value of X in the n trials is

$$\frac{n_1 x_1 + n_2 x_2 + \cdots n_k x_k}{n} = x_1 R_n(x_1) + x_2 R_n(x_2) + \cdots + x_k R_n(x_k)$$

where, for $i = 1, 2, \ldots, k$, $R_n(x_i)$ is the relative frequency of the value x_i in the n trials. Allowing n to increase indefinitely, so that $R_n(x_i)$ can be replaced by $p_i = P(X = x_i)$, the long-run average (mean) value of X is given by

$$x_1 p_1 + x_2 p_2 + \cdots + x_k p_k \equiv \sum_{i=1}^{k} x_i P(X = x_i), \tag{1}$$

which is defined to be the *expected value* of X and will be written as E(X).

Example 1

Find the expected number of heads that will be obtained when a fair coin is tossed three times.

Solution

Let X denote the number of heads that will be obtained. From Example 1 of Section 4.2, the distribution of X is as shown in the following table.

x	0	1	2	3
P(X = x)	$\frac{1}{8}$	$\frac{3}{8}$	$\frac{3}{8}$	$\frac{1}{8}$

Thus, from (1),

$$E(X) = 0 \times \frac{1}{8} + 1 \times \frac{3}{8} + 2 \times \frac{3}{8} + 3 \times \frac{1}{8} = 1\frac{1}{2}.$$

So the expected number of heads is 1½. Notice that this conflicts with one's everyday interpretation of the word 'expected', since no one would surely respond with the answer 1½ if asked to state how many heads one can expect when tossing a coin twice. It is important to appreciate the above definition of E(X) as being the average value of X in an *indefinitely* large number of trials of the underlying random experiment. As our example shows, the value of E(X) is not necessarily equal to one of the possible values of X.

Observe that the above distribution is symmetrical about x = 1½ = E(X). It is always true that for a random variable X whose distribution is symmetrical, E(X) is equal to the average of the possible values of X (the point of symmetry).

Example 2

Four balls are drawn at random without replacement from a bag containing 7 red balls and 6 blue balls. Find the expected number of red balls that will be drawn.

Solution

Let X denote the number of red balls drawn. We showed in Example 2 of Section 4.2 that the distribution of X is as follows:

x	0	1	2	3	4
P(X = x)	$\dfrac{3}{143}$	$\dfrac{28}{143}$	$\dfrac{63}{143}$	$\dfrac{42}{143}$	$\dfrac{7}{143}$

Hence, from (1)

$$E(X) = 0 \times \frac{3}{143} + 1 \times \frac{28}{143} + 2 \times \frac{63}{143} + 3 \times \frac{42}{143} + 4 \times \frac{7}{143} = \frac{308}{143} = 2.154$$

correct to three decimal places.

Example 3

Find the expected number of throws of a fair die until a score which is a multiple of 3 is obtained.

Solution

Let Y denote the number of throws required. We showed in Example 3 of Section 4.2 that the distribution of Y is:

$$P(Y = y) = pq^{y-1}, \text{ for } y = 1, 2, 3, 4, \ldots, \text{ where } p = 1/3 \text{ and } q = 1 - p = 2/3.$$

From (1) $E(Y) = 1 \times p + 2p \times q + 3p \times q^2 + 4p \times q^3 + \ldots,$

$$= p + 2pq + 3pq^2 + 4pq^3 + \ldots,$$

$$= p(1 + 2q + 3q^2 + 4q^3 + \ldots)$$

$$= p \frac{d}{dq}(q + q^2 + q^3 + q^4 + \cdots)$$

The series in the brackets is an infinite geometric series with first term a = q and common ratio r = q, whose sum is q/(1 – q). Differentiating this with respect to q gives $1/(1-q)^2 = 1/p^2$. Hence,

$$E(Y) = p \times \frac{1}{p^2} = \frac{1}{p}.$$

Since, in our example, p = 1/3, it follows that the expected number of throws is 3.

Exercise 4.3a

1. Find the expected value of X for each of the following distributions.

(a)

x	4	5	6
P(X = x)	$\frac{1}{6}$	$\frac{1}{2}$	$\frac{1}{3}$

(b)

x	0	1	2
P(X = x)	0.82	0.14	0.04

(c)

x	0	1	2	3	4
P(X = x)	$\frac{1}{6}$	$\frac{1}{12}$	$\frac{1}{4}$	$\frac{1}{3}$	$\frac{1}{6}$

(d)

x	1	2	3	4
P(X = x)	0.1	0.3	p	0.2

(e)

x	0	1	2	3
P(X = x)	α	α^2	$\alpha^2 + \alpha$	$3\alpha^2 + 2\alpha$

2. The random variable X has possible values 1 and 5 only. Given that E(X) = 4 evaluate P(X = 1).

3. A spinner is equally likely to give a score of 1, 2, 3, and 4. In one spin a player loses 10 p if the score is 1, wins 3 p is the score is 3, and wins 5 p if the score is 2 or 4. Find the player's expected gain per spin.

4. In a certain game a player pays 5 pence and throws a fair die. If a 6 is thrown the player will receive 15 pence; if an odd number is thrown the player will receive 5 pence; otherwise, the player receives nothing. Show that the game is fair in the sense that the player's expected gain per play is zero.

5. A person has three similar keys on a ring. Only one of these keys fits the lock of a particular door which the person wishes to unlock. The person chooses one key at random and tries it. If it is a wrong key the person chooses one of the other two keys at random. Find the expected number of keys tried by the person in order to open the door.

6. A litter of 8 mice consists of 3 females and 5 males. If a random sample of four mice is taken from the litter, find the expected number of female mice in the sample.

7. A box contains 4 white balls and 6 black balls.

(a)　If a random sample of 3 balls is to be drawn without replacement from the box, find the expected number of black balls that will be drawn.

(b)　If balls are to be drawn from the box one after another without replacement until a black ball is drawn, find the expected number of balls that will be drawn.

8.　A committee consists of 12 men and 8 women. Four of these are chosen at random to form a subcommittee. Find the expected number of women on the subcommittee.

9.　In any month the number, X, of a newagent's customers that will buy a copy of a specialist monthly magazine has the following distribution.

x	3	4	5	6
$P(X = x)$	0.4	0.3	0.2	0.1

The newsagent pays 50 p for each copy and sells it for £1. Any unsold copies at the end of a month have to be scrapped. The newsagent has to place an advance order for the number of copies to keep in stock each month. Find how many copies the newsagent should order each month in order to maximise the expected profit from the sale of the magazine.

Expected value of a function of a random variable

Let h(X) denote some function of the discrete random variable X whose distribution is

$$P(X = x_i) = p_i \text{ , for i = 1, 2, 3, ... , k.}$$

Definition. The *expected value* of h(X) is defined to be

$$E[h(X)] = h(x_1)p_1 + h(x_2)p_2 + h(x_3)p_3 + \cdots + h(x_k)p_k \equiv \sum_{i=1}^{k} h(x_i)p_i . \qquad (2)$$

Note that when h(X) = X this reduces to the expression we had for E(X).
Other examples are as follows.

$$E(X^2) = x_1^2 \times p_1 + x_2^2 \times p_2 + x_3^2 \times p_3 + \cdots + x_k^2 \times p_k$$

$$E(3X - 1) = (3x_1 - 1) \times p_1 + (3x_2 - 1) \times p_2 + ... + (3x_k - 1) \times p_k$$

Example 4

Find the expected value of the product of the number of heads and the number of tails when a fair coin is tossed three times.

Solution

Let X denote the number of heads in the three tosses, so that the number of tails tossed is (3 − X). The product of the number of heads and number of tails is Y = X(3 − X). We wish to find E(Y).

From Example 1 in Section 4.2, the distribution of X is:

x	0	1	2	3
$P(X = x)$	$\dfrac{1}{8}$	$\dfrac{3}{8}$	$\dfrac{3}{8}$	$\dfrac{1}{8}$

Using (2),

$$E(Y) = 0 \times (3-1) \times \frac{1}{8} + 1 \times (3-1) \times \frac{3}{8} + 2 \times (3-2) \times \frac{3}{8} + 3 \times (3-3) \times \frac{1}{8}$$

$$= 0 + \frac{3}{4} + \frac{3}{4} + 0 = 1\frac{1}{2}.$$

[Alternatively, we could have found $E(Y)$ by first deriving the distribution of Y from that of X; this is left as an exercise.]

A useful property of E

Let c_1 and c_2 denote constants and let $h_1(X)$ and $h_2(X)$ denote any two functions of X. Then

$$E[c_1 h_1(X) + c_2 h_2(X)] = c_1 E[h_1(X)] + c_2 E[h_2(X)], \tag{3}$$

which readily extends to a linear combination of three or more functions of X. The following particular cases are worthy of mention.

(1)   With $c_1 = c$ (a constant), $h_1(X) = 1$, and $c_2 = 0$, the above reduces to $E(c) = c$, which is obviously so, on recalling that E is a long-run average value.

(2)   With $c_1 = a$, $h_1(X) = X$, $c_2 = b$ and $h_2(X) = 1$, where a and b are constants, we have $E(aX + b) = aE(X) + b$; e.g. $E(5X - 3) = 5E(X) - 3$.

The following examples illustrate some other special cases of (3):

$$E(2X^2 + 3X) = 2E(X^2) + 3E(X) ,$$

$$E[(2X - 3)^2] \equiv E(4X^2 - 12X + 9) = 4E(X^2) - 12E(X) + 9.$$

Let us now prove (3). Suppose X has the distribution

$$P(X = x_i) = p_i \ , \text{ for } i = 1, 2, 3, \ldots , k.$$

From the definition given above we have

$$E[c_1 h_1(X) + c_2 h_2(X)] = \sum_{i=1}^{k} [c_1 h_1(x_i) + c_2 h_2(x_i)] p_i$$

$$= c_1 \sum h_1(x_i) p_i + c_2 \sum h_2(x_i) p_i$$

$$= c_1 E[h_1(X)] + c_2 E[h_2(X)].$$

We now have an alternative method for answering Example 4. In that example we wanted the expected value of $Y = X(3 - X)$, where X is the number of heads in three tosses of a fair coin. From the above property we have

$$E(Y) = E[X(3 - X)] = E(3X - X^2) = 3E(X) - E(X^2).$$

We have already found that $E(X) = 1\frac{1}{2}$ in Example 1. Using the distribution of X as given in Example 4 we find

$$E(X^2) = 0^2 \times \frac{1}{8} + 1^2 \times \frac{3}{8} + 2^2 \times \frac{3}{8} + 3^2 \times \frac{1}{8} = 3.$$

Hence,

$$E(Y) = 3E(X) - E(X^2) = 4\frac{1}{2} - 3 = 1\frac{1}{2},$$

as obtained in Example 4.

Exercise 4.3b

1. Use the above property of E to expand (a) $E(2X - 1)$, (b) $E(3 - 2X)$, (c) $E(3X^2 - 5X)$, (d) $E[X(2X - 3)]$, (e) $E[(X - 1)(2X + 3)]$.

2. For each of the distributions in Examples 1 and 2 above, verify that $E(X^2) \neq [E(X)]^2$.

3. The random variable X has possible values $x = 0, 1, 2$. Given that $P(X = 0) = P(X = 1) = p$ and that $E(X^2) = E(X)$, find the value of p.

4. The random variable X has the distribution
$$P(X = x) = \frac{3x+1}{22}, \text{ for } x = 0,1,2,3.$$
Find the values of (a) $E(X)$, (b) $E(X^2)$, (c) $E(2X^2 - 3X + 1)$.

5. The random variable X has the following distribution

x	1	2	3	4
$P(X = x)$	0.1	0.4	0.3	0.2

(a) Verify that $E\left(\frac{1}{X}\right) \neq \frac{1}{E(X)}$, (b) Evaluate $E(2X^2 - X + \frac{2}{X})$.

6. The random variable X has the following distribution.

x	1	4	9
$P(X = x)$	0.1	0.4	0.5

Evaluate (a) $E(X^2)$, (b) $E(X^{1/2})$.

7. Three balls are drawn at random without replacement from a box containing 3 red balls and 6 blue balls. Find the expected value of the product of the numbers of red balls and blue balls that are drawn.

4.4 Mean and variance of a distribution

Two useful summary features of a distribution are:

(1) a *measure of location, or central measure*, which gives an indication of the whereabouts of the distribution on a scaled line,

(2) a *measure of spread or dispersion* which gives an indication of the spread of the distribution.

The measure of location that we shall use is the *mean*, which is simply the value of E(X), the long-run average value of X, and will be denoted by the Greek letter μ.

The measure of spread that we shall use is the *standard deviation*. Before defining the standard deviation we shall first consider the *variance* of a distribution.

Definition. The *variance* of a distribution is defined to be

$$\text{Var}(X) = E[(X - \mu)^2] \qquad (1)$$

which will be denoted by σ^2, where σ is the Greek letter 'sigma'.

If X has the distribution

$$P(X = x_i) = p_i, \text{ for } i = 1, 2, 3, \dots, k,$$

and mean E(X) = μ, then from (2) of Section 4.3,

$$\text{Var}(X) = (x_1 - \mu)^2 p_1 + (x_2 - \mu)^2 p_2 + \dots + (x_k - \mu)^2 p_k. \qquad (2)$$

If X has units of measurement (e.g. cm) then Var(X) will have units which are the square of the units of X (e.g. cm^2). For this reason the measure of dispersion is usually taken to be the positive square root of Var(X), which is defined to be the *standard deviation* of the distribution, denoted by SD(X) or σ.

Example 1

Find the standard deviation of the random variable X whose distribution is as follows.

x	1	2	3	4
P(X = x)	0.1	0.4	0.3	0.2

Solution

We first need the value of μ = E(X).

$$E(X) = 1 \times 0.1 + 2 \times 0.4 + 3 \times 0.3 + 4 \times 0.2 = 2.6.$$

Using (2) we have

$$\text{Var}(X) = (1 - 2.6)^2 \times 0.1 + (2 - 2.6)^2 \times 0.4 + (3 - 2.6)^2 \times 0.3 + (4 - 2.6)^2 \times 0.2$$
$$= 2.56 \times 0.1 + 0.36 \times 0.4 + 0.16 \times 0.3 + 1.96 \times 0.2 = 0.84.$$

The standard deviation is

$$SD(X) = \sqrt{0.84} = 0.9165, \text{ correct to four decimal places.}$$

On expanding (1) we have

$$\text{Var}(X) = E(X^2 - 2\mu X + \mu^2)$$
$$= E(X^2) - 2\mu E(X) + \mu^2, \text{ since } \mu \text{ is a constant.}$$

Replacing μ by $E(X)$ and simplifying we have

$$\text{Var}(X) = E(X^2) - [E(X)]^2, \tag{3}$$

which is very often a more convenient formula for finding a variance, particularly when $E(X)$ is not an integer, which was the case in Example 1 above (even though X could only take integer values).

For the distribution in Example 1 we have

$$E(X^2) = 1^2 \times 0.1 + 2^2 \times 0.4 + 3^2 \times 0.3 + 4^2 \times 0.2 = 7.6.$$

Using (3) and the value $E(X) = 2.6$ obtained above,

$$\text{Var}(X) = 7.6 - 2.6^2 = 0.84,$$

as obtained using (1) in Example 1.

Example 2

Four balls are drawn at random without replacement from a bag containing 7 red balls and 6 blue balls. Find the distribution of the number of red balls drawn and determine the mean and standard deviation of the distribution.

Solution

From Example 2 of Section 4.2, the distribution of X = the number of red balls drawn is as follows.

x	0	1	2	3	4
P(X = x)	$\dfrac{3}{143}$	$\dfrac{28}{143}$	$\dfrac{63}{143}$	$\dfrac{42}{143}$	$\dfrac{7}{143}$

In Example 2 of Section 4.3 we showed that $E(X) = 308/143 = 28/13$.

$$E(X^2) = 0^2 \times \frac{3}{143} + 1^2 \times \frac{28}{143} + 2^2 \times \frac{63}{143} + 3^2 \times \frac{42}{143} + 4^2 \times \frac{7}{143} = \frac{770}{143} = \frac{70}{13}.$$

Using (3) we then have

$$\text{Var}(X) = \frac{70}{13} - \left(\frac{28}{13}\right)^2 = \frac{126}{169},$$

and the standard deviation is

$$\text{SD}(X) = \sqrt{(126/169)} = 0.863, \text{ correct to three decimal places.}$$

Example 3

The random variable X has mean 8.4 and standard deviation 2.4. Find the value of $E(X^2)$.

Solution

Using (3) we have

$$Var(X) = E(X^2) - [E(X)]^2 .$$

Substituting the given values for $E(X)$ and $SD(X)$,

$$2.4^2 = E(X^2) - 8.4^2$$

so that

$$E(X^2) = 2.4^2 + 8.4^2 = 76.32.$$

Exercise 4.4a

1. Find the mean and, to three significant figures, the standard deviation of each of the following distributions.

(a)

x	1	2	3
$P(X = x)$	0.2	0.4	0.4

(b)

x	0	1	2	3	4
$P(X = x)$	0.1	0.1	0.3	0.3	0.2

(c)

x	5	10	15	20
$P(X = x)$	$\dfrac{1}{8}$	$\dfrac{1}{4}$	$\dfrac{3}{8}$	$\dfrac{1}{4}$

(d) $P(X = x) = kx^3$, $x = 1, 2, 3, 4$.

2. A box contains 3 red balls and 6 white balls.

(a) Three balls are to be drawn at random without replacement from the box. Let X denote the number of red balls that will be drawn. Find the mean and the variance of X.

(b) Instead, balls are to be drawn at random one after another without replacement from the box until a white ball is drawn. Let Y denote the number of balls that will be drawn. Find the mean and variance of Y.

3. A bag contains five cards which are numbered from 1 to 5, respectively. Three cards are drawn at random without replacement from the bag. Find the mean and variance of the **largest** of the numbers drawn.

4. In a certain game a player tosses a fair coin and then throws a fair cubical die. If the coin shows tails the player's score is the number showing on the die, but if the coin shows

heads the player's score is twice the number showing on the die. Find the mean and, to three significant figures, the standard deviation of the player's score.

5.   The random variable X has mean 20.7 and standard deviation 3.5. Find the value of $E(X^2)$.

Mean and variance of a linear function

Consider the random variable $Y = aX + b$, where a and b are constants and X is distributed with mean $E(X)$ and variance $Var(X)$. What are the mean and the variance of Y? If we knew the distribution of X completely we could deduce the distribution of Y and use it to find $E(Y)$ and $Var(Y)$. As it happens we can find the mean and the variance of Y without knowing its distribution. Using the properties of E given in Section 4.3 the mean of Y is

$$E(Y) = E(aX + b) = aE(X) + b.$$

The variance of Y by definition is

$$\begin{aligned} Var(Y) &= E(Y^2) - [E(Y)]^2 \\ &= E(a^2X^2 + 2abX + b^2) - [a^2E^2(X) + 2abE(X) + b^2] \\ &= a^2[E(X^2) - E^2(X)] = a^2Var(X). \end{aligned}$$

For example:

(a)   If $Y = 2X - 3$, then $E(Y) = 2E(X) - 3$, and $Var(Y) = 4Var(X)$.

(b)   If $W = 5 - 6X$, then $E(W) = 5 - 6E(X)$ and $Var(W) = 36Var(X)$.

Example 4

With reference to Example 2 above, suppose that each red ball drawn scores 2 points and each blue ball drawn scores 4 points. Find the mean and the variance of the combined score for the four balls that are drawn.

Solution

Let X denote the number of red balls drawn. Then the number of blue balls drawn is $4 - X$ and the combined score for the four balls is

$$T = 2X + 4(4 - X) = 16 - 2X.$$

Using results obtained earlier for $E(X)$ and $Var(X)$,

$$E(T) = 16 - 2E(X) = 16 - 2 \times \frac{28}{13} = \frac{152}{13},$$

$$Var(T) = 4\,Var(X) = 4 \times \frac{126}{169} = \frac{504}{169}.$$

Exercise 4.4b

1. The random variable X has mean 10 and standard deviation 2. Find the mean and the standard deviation of (a) $Y = X + 1$, (b) $Z = 2X$, (c) $W = 3X - 5$, (d) $T = 1 - 2X$, (e) $U = \frac{1}{2}(X - 2)$.

2. The random variable X has mean 8 and standard deviation 4. Find the values of a and b if $Y = aX + b$ has mean zero and standard deviation 1.

3. A car salesperson is paid a fixed weekly wage of £180 per week and a commission of £120 on each new car the person sells. The number of new cars sold per week by this person is a discrete random variable having mean 1.96 and standard deviation 1.48. Find the mean and the standard deviation of the salesperson's weekly earnings.

4. Three balls are drawn at random without replacement from a box containing 3 red balls and 7 white balls. Let X denote the number of red balls drawn. Calculate the mean and the standard deviation of X. If each red ball drawn scores 3 points and each white ball drawn scores 1 point, deduce the mean and the standard deviation of the total score for the three balls that are drawn.

5. In a multiple choice test paper there are 50 questions. The number answered correctly is a discrete random variable having mean 22 and standard deviation 4. Each correct answer earns 4 marks while 1 mark is deducted for each incorrect answer and for each question which is not attempted. Find the mean and the standard deviation of the marks scored.

6. The random variable X has the following distribution,
$$P(X = x) = kx^2, \qquad \text{for } x = 1, 2, 3,$$
$$P(X = x) = k(7 - x)^2, \quad \text{for } x = 4, 5, 6.$$
Find the mean and the variance of X. Deduce the mean and the variance of
(a) $Y = 2X - 1$, (b) $W = 2(4 - X)$.

7. The random variable X is such that $E(X) = 1$ and $E[X(X - 1)] = 4$. Evaluate
(a) $Var(X)$, (b) $Var(2 - 3X)$.

4.5 The binomial distribution

Consider a random experiment having only two possible outcomes, which is often referred to as a *Bernoulli trial*. We shall label one of the outcomes as S, a 'success', and the other as F, a 'failure'. Let p be the probability of a success in each trial (performance) of the experiment. [The tossing of a coin is an example of such an experiment; if the coin is fair and a head is regarded as being a success, then $p = \frac{1}{2}$]. Let X denote the number of successes that will be obtained in n independent trials of the experiment. The distribution of X has a standard form known as the *binomial distribution*. Before we derive this distribution let us consider some examples.

Example 1

For a random experiment, in each trial of which the probability of a success is p, find the distribution of the number of successes in (a) three independent trials, (b) five independent trials.

Solution

(a) Let X denote the number of successes in three trials. The possible values of X are x = 0, 1, 2 and 3.

X = 0 occurs only if all three trials give a failure. Since the probability of a failure in any trial is q = 1 − p, and the trials are independent, $P(X = 0) = q \times q \times q = q^3$.

X = 1 occurs if one trial gives a success and the other two give a failure. The ordered possibilities are (SFF), (FSF), and (FFS). Each of these has probability pq^2, so that $P(X = 1) = 3pq^2$.

X = 2 occurs if the ordered outcome is one of (SSF), (SFS), and (FSS), each of which has probability p^2q, so that $P(X = 2) = 3p^2q$.

Finally, X = 3 occurs if the ordered outcome is (SSS), so that $P(X = 3) = p^3$. Thus, the distribution of X is as follows:

x	0	1	2	3
P(X = x)	q^3	$3pq^2$	$3p^2q$	p^3

Observe that the four probabilities are the successive terms in the binomial expansion of $(q + p)^3$ and that they sum to 1 (since p + q = 1).

(b) Let X denote the number of successes in five trials. The possible values of this X are x = 0, 1, 2, 3, 4, and 5.

X = 0 occurs if all five trials give a failure, so that $P(X = 0) = q^5$.

X = 1 occurs if four of the trials give a failure and one gives a success. The number of ordered outcomes leading to X = 1 is equivalent to the number of ways of choosing one of the five trials to be a failure, which is $\binom{5}{1} = 5$. Each of these will have a probability which is the product of one p and four q's, namely pq^4, so that $P(X = 1) = 5pq^4$.

X = 2 occurs if the ordered outcome consists of two successes and three failures. The number of such outcomes is $\binom{5}{2} = 10$, and each has probability p^2q^3, so that $P(X = 2) = 10p^2q^3$.

Similarly we find that

$$P(X = 3) = \binom{5}{3}p^3q^2 = 10p^3q^2.$$

$$P(X = 4) = \binom{5}{4}p^4q = 5p^4q \quad \text{and} \quad P(X = 5) = p^5.$$

Thus, the probabilities that X takes the values 0, 1, 2, 3 4, 5 are, respectively,

$q^5, 5pq^4, 10p^2q^3, 10p^3q^2, 5p^4q, p^5,$

which are the successive terms in the binomial expansion of $(q + p)^5$.

Now consider the general case where X is the number of successes in n independent trials. The possible values of X are x = 0, 1, 2, ..., n. Let x be an arbitrary one of these values. Then X = x occurs if the ordered outcome consists of x successes and (n − x) failures. The number of such outcomes is $\binom{n}{x}$. Each such outcome will consist of S occurring x times and F occurring (n − x) times and its probability is a product (in some order) in which p occurs x times and q = 1 − p occurs (n − x) times, so that each of these ordered outcomes has probability p^xq^{n-x}. Thus, the distribution of X is:

$$P(X = x) = \binom{n}{x}p^xq^{n-x} \quad , \text{for } x = 0, 1, 2, ..., n. \tag{1}$$

The probabilities in (1) are the successive terms in the expansion of $(q + p)^n$ and sum to unity. A random variable X having the distribution given in (1) is said to be *binomially distributed* with index n and success probability p. We shall abbreviate this as X~B(n, p), where ~ stands for "has the distribution".

When p = q = ½, (1) reduces to

$$P(X = x) = \binom{n}{x}\left(\frac{1}{2}\right)^n.$$

Since $\binom{n}{x} = \binom{n}{n-x}$ this distribution is symmetrical about the mid-value $x = \frac{1}{2}n$. This is illustrated for the distribution B(6, 0.5) in Figure 1. For p ≠ 0.5, the B(n, p) distribution will be skew, as illustrated in Figures 2 and 3 for the distributions B(6, 0.4) and B(6, 0.7).

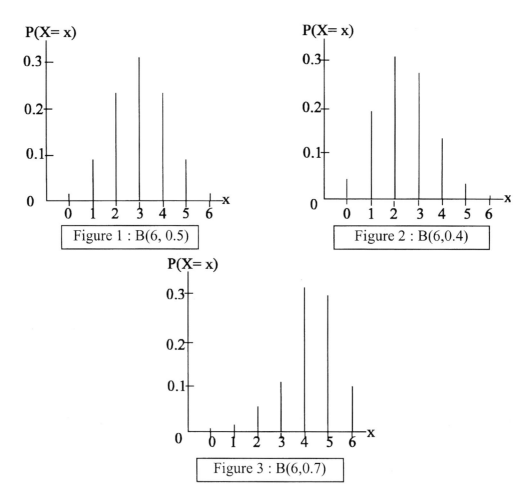

Figure 1 : B(6, 0.5)

Figure 2 : B(6,0.4)

Figure 3 : B(6,0.7)

Example 2

Find the probability that in 12 throws of a fair die a score of 6 will be obtained (a) exactly twice, (b) at least twice.

Solution

Since the die is fair, the probability of a 6 in any throw is 1/6. Let X denote the number 6's obtained in 12 throws of the die. Then X has the binomial distribution $B\left(12, \frac{1}{6}\right)$; that is

$$P(X = x) = \binom{12}{x}\left(\frac{1}{6}\right)^{x}\left(\frac{5}{6}\right)^{12-x} \text{, for } x = 0, 1, 2, 3, \dots, 12.$$

(a) $P(X = 2) = \binom{12}{2}\left(\frac{1}{6}\right)^{2}\left(\frac{5}{6}\right)^{10} = \frac{66 \times 5^{10}}{6^{12}} = 0.296,$

correct to three decimal places.

(b) $P(X \geq 2) = P(X = 2) + P(X = 3) + \ldots + P(X = 12)$.

Here it is much simpler to find the probability of the complementary event and to use

$$P(X \geq 2) = 1 - P(X < 2) = 1 - \{P(X = 0) + P(X = 1)\}$$

$$= 1 - \left\{ \left(\frac{5}{6}\right)^{12} + \binom{12}{1}\left(\frac{1}{6}\right)\left(\frac{5}{6}\right)^{11} \right\}$$

$$= 1 - 0.381 = 0.619, \text{ correct to three decimal places.}$$

Exercise 4.5a

1.   The random variable X has the distribution B(n, p). For each of the cases when
      (a) n = 6, p = 0.4 and (b) n = 8, p = 0.3, calculate, correct to three decimal places, the
      values of (i) P(X = 3), (ii) P(X ≥ 3).

2.   A fair coin is tossed ten times. Calculate the probabilities, correct to three decimal
      places, of obtaining (a) exactly two heads, (b) at most two heads, (c) at least two heads,
      (d) more than two heads.

3.   Find, correct to three decimal places, the probability of throwing at least two 6's in five
      throws of a fair die. Find also the most probable number of 6's that will be thrown.

4.   Assuming that each child in a family of three children is equally likely to be a boy or a
      girl, calculate the probabilities that in a family of three children there will be
      (a) exactly one boy, (b) at least one boy, (c) at least two boys.

5.   A multiple-choice test paper has 8 questions, each of which offers four possible answers
      only one of which is correct. For a candidate who guesses the answer to each question
      calculate the probabilities that this candidate will have the correct answers to (a) exactly
      3 questions, (b) at least 6 questions.

6.   A biased coin is such that when tossed the probability of obtaining a head is 2/3. The
      coin is to be tossed five times. Find the probabilities that the number of heads tossed
      will be (a) exactly 3, (b) more than 3.

7.   Independently for each shot fired at a target by a particular person, the probability that
      the shot will hit the target is 0.75. If the person fires 7 shots, find the probability that
      (a) exactly 3 will hit the target, (b) at most 3 will hit the target.

8.   The probability that a randomly chosen tulip bulb will produce a yellow flower is 0.7.
      Find the probabilities that 10 randomly chosen bulbs will produce (a) exactly 6 yellow
      flowers, (b) at least 8 yellow flowers. Give your answers correct to 3 decimal places.

9.   Each of two persons tosses three fair coins. Find the probability that they will toss equal
      numbers of heads.

10. (a) Find the most probable value, or values, of X in each of the cases when

(i) $X \sim B(6, 0.3)$, (ii) $X \sim B(4, 0.4)$.

(b) The random variable X has the binomial distribution B(n, p). Show that

$$\frac{p_{x+1}}{p_x} = \frac{(n-x)p}{(x+1)q}$$

where $q = 1 - p$ and $p_x = P(X = x)$. Hence show that

(i) if $(n + 1)p$ is not an integer then X has a unique most probable value when x is the largest integer less than $(n + 1)p$;

(ii) if $(n + 1)p$ is an integer then X has two equally most probable values when $x = (n + 1)p - 1$ and $x = (n + 1)p$.

Use of tables

Evaluation of binomial probabilities can be very cumbersome, particularly when n is large. For example, consider evaluating $P(X \le 26)$ when X has the distribution B(50, 0.6). For this reason, tables have been prepared to ease the burden. Some tables give the values of $P(X = x)$, others give the values of $P(X \le x)$ or $P(X \ge x)$, for selected values of n and of $p \le 0.5$. *Elementary Statistical Tables* published by RND (Cardiff) gives the values of $P(X \le x)$ while *Statistical Tables* by Murdoch and Barnes gives the values of $P(X \ge x)$, each correct to four decimal places. The following results are useful when using such tables.

$$P(X = x) \equiv P(X \le x) - P(X \le x - 1) \equiv P(X \ge x) - P(X \ge x + 1),$$
$$P(X \ge x) \equiv 1 - P(X \le x - 1) \quad ; \quad P(X \le x) \equiv 1 - P(X \ge x + 1),$$
$$P(r \le X \le s) \equiv P(X \le s) - P(X \le r - 1) \equiv P(X \ge r) - P(X \ge s + 1).$$

The following examples illustrate the use of tables, the solutions given being based on tables which give the values of $P(X \le x)$. These will need to be modified slightly if the tables used give the values of $P(X \ge x)$.

Example 3

Given that X has the distribution B(20, 0.4) find, correct to three decimal places, the values of
(a) $P(X = 5)$, (b) $P(4 \le X \le 12)$, (c) $P(X > 8)$.

Solution

(a) $\qquad P(X = 5) \equiv P(X \le 5) - P(X \le 4) = 0.1256 - 0.0510$
$\qquad\qquad\qquad\qquad\qquad\qquad = 0.075$ correct to three decimal places.

(b) $\qquad P(4 \le X \le 12) \equiv P(X \le 12) - P(X \le 3) = 0.9790 - 0.0160$
$\qquad\qquad\qquad\qquad\qquad\qquad = 0.963$ correct to three decimal places.

(c) $\qquad P(X > 8) \equiv 1 - P(X \le 8) = 1 - 0.5956$
$\qquad\qquad\qquad\qquad\qquad\qquad = 0.404$ correct to three decimal places.

As mentioned above, tables normally restrict values of p to be ≤ 0.5. However, such tables can still be used to evaluate binomial probabilities when p is > 0.5. Suppose that X has the distribution B(n, p) where p has a value bigger than 0.5. Recall that X is the number of successes in n trials of a random experiment in each of which the probability of a success is p. The number of failures in those trials is $Y = n - X$ whose distribution is B(n, q), where $q = 1 - p$ is < 0.5. Thus, the tables can be used to determine the probability of any event involving X by finding the equivalent event involving $Y = n - X$. This is illustrated in the following example.

Example 4

Given that X has the distribution B(50, 0.7) find, correct to three decimal places, the values of (a) P(X = 30), (b) P(25 $\leq$ X $\leq$ 35).

Solution

Let $Y = 50 - X$; then Y has the distribution B(50, 0.3).

(a)   X = 30 (successes) is equivalent to Y = 20 (failures). Hence

$$P(X = 30) \equiv P(Y = 20) \equiv P(Y \leq 20) - P(Y \leq 19) = 0.9522 - 0.9152$$
$$= 0.037 \text{ correct to three decimal places.}$$

(b)   A number of successes ranging from 25 to 35 is equivalent to a number of failures ranging from 15 to 25. Hence

$$P(25 \leq X \leq 35) \equiv P(15 \leq Y \leq 25) = P(Y \leq 25) - P(Y \leq 14) = 0.9991 - 0.4468$$
$$= 0.552 \text{ correct to three decimal places.}$$

Exercise 4.5b

In each of the following use your tables to evaluate the required probabilities correct to three decimal places.

1.   Given that X has the distribution B(20, 0.25), evaluate   (a) P(X = 8),   (b) P(X > 5), (c) P(5 $\leq$ X $\leq$ 10).

2.   Given that X has the distribution B(50, 0.4), evaluate   (a) P(X = 12),   (b) P(X $\leq$ 16), (c) P (X $\geq$ 18),   (d) P(12 $\leq$ X $\leq$ 17).

3.   If a fair coin is tossed 50 times, find the probability that the number of heads obtained will be from 20 to 30, inclusive.

4.   The random variable X has the distribution B(n, p). Evaluate P(X $\geq$ np) in each of the cases (a) n = 20, p = 0.8, (b) n = 10, p = 0.25.

5. The probability that a randomly chosen tulip bulb will produce a yellow flower is 0.6. If 20 such bulbs are planted find the probabilities that (a) exactly 10 of them will produce yellow flowers, (b) from 5 to 10 of them, inclusive, will produce yellow flowers.

6. A multiple-choice test paper has 50 questions, each of which offers four possible answers, only one of which is correct. For a candidate who guesses the answer to each question, calculate the probability that the number of questions that will be answered correctly is (a) exactly 11, (b) from 10 to 20, inclusive.

7. During a practice session a rugby player takes kicks at goal from various distances. Independently for each kick from a distance of d metres the player's probability of succeeding is 0.02 (60 − d). Find the probability that the number of successful kicks will be (a) exactly 6, (b) at least 6, in each of the cases when the player takes (i) 10 kicks from a distance of 20 metres, (ii) 20 kicks from a distance of 40 metres. Give one reason why the binomial distribution may not be appropriate in the situation described here.

8. A school has a total of 1600 pupils including 400 of Asian origin. In a random sample of 50 pupils from the school, let X denote the number of Asian origin in the sample.

(a) Explain why the binomial distribution cannot be used as an exact model for the distribution of X but is appropriate as an approximate model.

(b) Use the binomial approximate model to calculate, to 3 decimal places, the probability that exactly 15 of the sampled pupils are of Asian origin.

Mean and variance of B(n, p)

If $X \sim B(n, p)$ then the mean and variance of X are:
$$\mu \equiv E(X) = np \quad \text{and} \quad \sigma^2 \equiv Var(X) = npq.$$

[The derivations of these results given below are algebraically complicated. A much simpler method will be given in book 2].

Proof $E(X) = \sum_{x=0}^{n} xP(X = x) = \sum_{x=1}^{n} x\binom{n}{x}p^x q^{n-x}$.

Now

$$x\binom{n}{x} \equiv x \times \frac{n!}{x!(n-x)!} = n \times \frac{(n-1)!}{(x-1)!(n-x)!} = n \times \binom{n-1}{x-1}$$

so that

$$\mu = E(X) = n \times \sum_{x=1}^{n} \binom{n-1}{x-1} p^x q^{n-x} = np \times \sum_{x=1}^{n} \binom{n-1}{x-1} p^{x-1} q^{n-x}$$

$$= np \left\{ q^{n-1} + \binom{n-1}{1} pq^{n-2} + \binom{n-1}{2} p^2 q^{n-3} + \cdots + p^{n-1} \right\}$$

$$= np(q+p)^{n-1} = np, \text{ since } p+q = 1.$$

$$E(X^2) = \sum_{x=0}^{n} x^2 \binom{n}{x} p^x q^{n-x} = \sum_{x=1}^{n} x^2 \binom{n}{x} p^x q^{n-x}.$$

Now, for $1 \leq x \leq n$,

$$x^2 \binom{n}{x} = x^2 \times \frac{n!}{x!(n-x)!} = x \times \frac{n!}{(x-1)!(n-x)!}.$$

Using the identity $x \equiv (x-1) + 1$, we have

$$x^2 \binom{n}{x} = \frac{n!}{(x-2)!(n-x)!} + \frac{n!}{(x-1)!(n-x)!}$$

$$= n(n-1) \times \binom{n-2}{x-2} + n \times \binom{n-1}{x-1}$$

Hence,

$$E(X^2) = n(n-1) \times \sum_{x=2}^{n} \binom{n-2}{x-2} p^x q^{n-x} + n \times \sum_{x=1}^{n} \binom{n-1}{x-1} p^x q^{n-x},$$

$$= n(n-1)p^2(q+p)^{n-2} + np(q+p)^{n-1}$$

$$= n(n-1)p^2 + np$$

It follows that

$$\text{Var}(X) \equiv E(X^2) - \mu^2 = n(n-1)p^2 + np - (np)^2$$
$$= n^2p^2 - np^2 + np - n^2p^2 = np(1-p) = npq.$$

Example 5

Verify these results for the distribution B(3, p).

In Example 1 we showed that the distribution B(3, p) is:

x	0	1	2	3
P(X = x)	q^3	$3pq^2$	$3p^2q$	p^3

Solution

For this distribution

$$E(X) = 0 \times q^3 + 1 \times 3pq^2 + 2 \times 3p^2q + 3 \times p^3$$

$$= 3pq^2 + 6p^2q + 3p^3 = 3p(q + p)^2 = 3p,$$

verifying the above result for n = 3.

$$E(X^2) = 3pq^2 + 12p^2q + 9p^3 = 3p(q + p)(q + 3p) = 3p(q + 3p).$$

$$Var(X) = 3p(q + 3p) - (3p)^2 = 3pq$$

verifying the result given above for n = 3.

Example 6

Given that the mean and standard deviation of a binomial distribution are 3.2 and 1.6, respectively, find the values of n and p.

Solution

We are given that np = 3.2 and np(1 − p) = 1.6^2 = 2.56.

Substituting from the first of these equations in the second we have

$$3.2(1 − p) = 2.56,$$

so that $\qquad$ 1 − p = 2.56/3.2 = 0.8 and p = 0.2.

Since np = 3.2 it follows that n = 3.2/0.2 = 16.

Exercise 4.5c

1. Let X denote the number of 6's obtained in four throws of a fair die. Identify the distribution of X and write down the values of its mean and variance. Verify your answers by first constructing a table to show the distribution of X.

2. Given that X ~ B(10, p), where p < 0.5, and that Var(X) = 15/8 find (a) p, (b) E(X), and (c) P(X = 2).

3. In each trial of a random experiment the probability of a success is 0.2. Find the number of independent trials that need to be conducted if the mean of the distribution of the number of successes in the n trials is to be equal to its standard deviation.

4. The random variable X has the distribution B(n, 0.8).

Given that $P(X = 3) = 8P(X = 2)$, find the mean of the distribution.

5. Find the values of n and p of the binomial distribution whose mean is 3.5 and whose variance is 1.05.

6. A door-to-door salesperson is paid a basic salary of £100 per week and a commission of £5 on each sale made. Suppose the salesperson makes 100 calls per week and that the probability that a call results in a sale is 0.2. Identify the distribution of the number of sales made per week and write down its mean and variance. Deduce the mean and the standard deviation of the salesperson's earnings per week.

7. A person pays 10 pence and tosses 5 fair coins simultaneously. If the person tosses X heads he will be paid X^2 pence. Find the person's expected loss per throw.

4.6 The Poisson distribution

In this section we shall need to use the following exponential series expansion:

$$e^\alpha = 1 + \alpha + \frac{\alpha^2}{2!} + \frac{\alpha^3}{3!} + \cdots + \frac{\alpha^r}{r!} + \cdots \tag{1}$$

Let X denote a random variable having the distribution

$$P(X = x) = \frac{\alpha^x}{x!} e^{-\alpha}, \qquad \text{for } x = 0, 1, 2, 3, \ldots \tag{2}$$

Note that

$$\sum_{x=0}^{\infty} P(X = x) = \sum_{x=0}^{\infty} \frac{\alpha^x}{x!} e^{-\alpha}$$

$$= e^{-\alpha} \left(1 + \alpha + \frac{\alpha^2}{2!} + \frac{\alpha^3}{3!} + \cdots + \frac{\alpha^r}{r!} + \cdots \right)$$

$$= e^{-\alpha} \times e^\alpha = 1,$$

as is required of a probability distribution. A random variable having the distribution (2) is said to have the *Poisson* distribution with parameter α, which we shall abbreviate as $X \sim \text{Po}(\alpha)$. We will show later that α is in fact the mean of this distribution, so that in keeping with our earlier notation α may be replaced by μ. Figures 4 and 5 show the forms of the distributions Po(2) and Po(6), respectively.

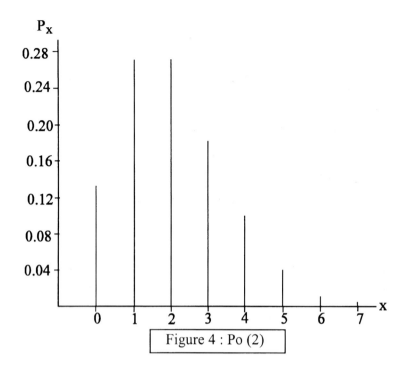

Figure 4 : Po (2)

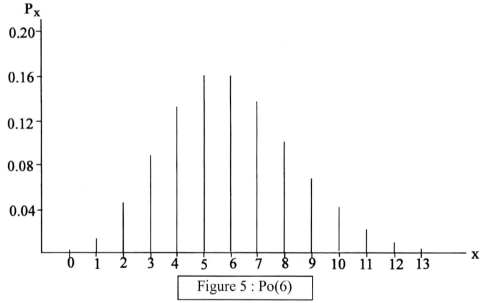

Figure 5 : Po(6)

This distribution has been found to be an appropriate model for the distribution of the number of times that an event occurs in an interval of time or space. In fact, the above distribution can be determined mathematically on the assumptions that

(a)   the events occur at random and independently over time or space,

(b)   the events occur singly,

(c)   the average number of occurrences of the event in a fixed interval of time or space is directly proportional to the width of that interval.

Some examples of random variables satisfying the above conditions, at least approximately, are as follows:

(1) The number of incoming telephone calls to an office during a specified time period.

(2) The number of emissions from a given radioactive source in a specified time period.

(3) The number of cars passing a certain point in a given time period.

(4) The number of flaws along a specified length of material or cable.

(5) The number of blood cells that are visible under a microscope.

(6) The number of organic particles suspended in a given volume of liquid.

Example 1

The distribution of the number of accidents per month in a factory can be modelled by a Poisson distribution, the average number of accidents per month being 2.6. Calculate the probability that there will be fewer than 3 accidents in a month.

Solution

Let X denote the number of accidents in a month. Then, $X \sim Po(2.6)$; that is

$$P(X = x) = \frac{2.6^x}{x!} e^{-2.6} \quad , \text{ for } x = 0,1,2,3,\cdots$$

$$P(X < 3) = P(X = 0) + P(X = 1) + P(X = 2)$$

$$= e^{-2.6}\left(1 + 2.6 + \frac{2.6^2}{2!}\right) = e^{-2.6} \times 6.98 = 0.518 \,,$$

correct to three decimal places.

Example 2

The number of flaws occurring in a given length of curtain material may be assumed to have a Poisson distribution. The mean number of flaws occurring per 10 metres of the material is 0.8. Calculate the probability that (a) a length of 10 metres of the material contains no flaw, (b) a length of 30 metres of the material contains at least 4 flaws.

Solution

(a) Let X denote the number of flaws in a length of 10 metres. Then $X \sim Po(0.8)$, so that

$$P(X = 0) = \frac{0.8^x}{x!} \times e^{-0.8}, \qquad \text{for } x = 0, 1, 2, 3, \ldots$$

$$P(X = 0) = e^{-0.8} = 0.449, \text{ correct to three decimal places.}$$

(b)   Let Y denote the number of flaws in a length of 30 metres. The average number of flaws in lengths of 30 metres is $3 \times 0.8 = 2.4$, so that $Y \sim Po(2.4)$ and

$$P(Y = y) = \frac{2.4^y}{y!} \times e^{-2.4} \ , \ \text{for } y = 0,1,2,3,\cdots$$

$$P(Y \geq 4) = 1 - P(Y \leq 3) = 1 - \{P(Y = 0) + P(Y = 1) + P(Y = 2) + P(Y = 3)\}$$

$$= 1 - e^{-2.4}\left(1 + 2.4 + \frac{2.4^2}{2!} + \frac{2.4^3}{3!}\right)$$

$$= 1 - e^{-2.4} \times 8.584 = 0.221, \text{ correct to three decimal places.}$$

Example 3

A small garage has three cars available for daily hire. The daily demand for these cars has a Poisson distribution with mean 2. The owner charges £25 per day, per car hired, but has total outgoings on the three cars amounting to £10 per day, irrespective of the number of cars actually hired. Find the owner's expected daily profit from hiring these cars.

Solution

Let X denote the demand for cars on a day. Then $X \sim Po(2)$.

Let Y denote the number actually hired on a day. Since there are only 3 cars available, the possible values of Y are $y = 0, 1, 2, 3$, with $y = 3$ when $X \geq 3$.

Let £Z denote the profit on a day. Since the total outgoings amount to £10 and each car hired brings in £25, it follows that $Z = 25Y - 10$ and

$$E(Z) = 25E(Y) - 10.$$

Let us now find the distribution of Y.

$$P(Y = 0) = P(X = 0) = e^{-2}.$$
$$P(Y = 1) = P(X = 1) = 2e^{-2}.$$
$$P(Y = 2) = P(X = 2) = (2^2/2)e^{-2} = 2e^{-2}.$$
$$P(Y = 3) = 1 - [P(Y = 0) + P(Y = 1) + P(Y = 2)] = 1 - 5e^{-2}.$$

Then

$$E(Y) = 0 \times e^{-2} + 1 \times 2e^{-2} + 2 \times 2e^{-2} + 3(1 - 5e^{-2})$$
$$= 3 - 9e^{-2},$$

and $$E(Z) = 25(3 - 9e^{-2}) - 10 = 65 - 225e^{-2}$$
$$= 34.550 \quad \text{correct to 3 decimal places.}$$

It follows that the expected daily profit is £34.55 correct to the nearest penny.

Exercise 4.6a

In each of the following give your answer correct to 3 decimal places.

1. Given that $X \sim Po(3)$, evaluate (a) $P(X = 3)$, (b) $P(X \le 2)$, (c) $P(X > 4)$.

2. Given that $X \sim Po(2.8)$ evaluate (a) $P(X = 4)$, (b) $P(X < 3)$.

3. Given that $P(X = 2) = 3P(X = 4)$ and that X has a Poisson distribution, find the values of (a) $P(X = 0)$ and (b) $P(X \le 4)$.

4. The number of raisins per slice of fruit cake may be assumed to have a Poisson distribution with mean 5. Calculate the probability that (a) one slice of the cake will contain (i) exactly 5 raisins, (ii) no more than 3 raisins, (b) two slices of the cake will contain exactly 5 raisins.

5. The number of bacteria per millilitre of inoculum has a Poisson distribution with mean 2.5. Find the probability that 1 millilitre of the inoculum will contain (a) exactly 3 bacteria, (b) at least 3 bacteria.

6. The number of flaws per 10 metre length of manufactured material has a Poisson distribution with mean 1.2. Calculate the probability that (a) a length of 10 metres will contain at most 2 flaws, (b) a length of 20 metres will contain at least 4 flaws.

7. Each of ten test-tubes containing nutrient material is inoculated with 1 cc of liquid containing an average 3 bacteria per cc. Under reasonable assumptions, which should be stated, calculate the probability that exactly 7 of the 10 test-tubes will contain at least one bacterium.

8. Each month a newsagent receives 15 copies of a monthly magazine, of which 10 have been ordered by customers. The monthly demand for the remaining 5 copies may be modelled by a Poisson distribution with mean 4. Let X denote the number of copies that will be sold in a month.

(a) Find, in terms of e, the probabilities that X will take the values 10, 11, 12, 13, 14 and 15. Hence calculate the expected value of X correct to two decimal places.

(b) The newsagent makes a profit of 30 pence on each copy sold but suffers a loss of 10 pence on each copy which is unsold during a month.

Find the expected monthly profit from the sale of this magazine.

(c) Assuming that the distribution of the monthly demand remains unchanged, determine whether it would be financially beneficial for the newsagent to reduce the number of copies received from 15 to 14.

Use of tables

As in the case of the binomial distribution, tables have been prepared for evaluating Poisson probabilities for selected values of μ. In the following example we have used a table giving the values of $P(X \leq x)$, where X has a Poisson distribution. The solutions given here will need to be modified if your table gives the values of $P(X \geq x)$.

Example 4

The number of incoming calls per hour to a switchboard has the Poisson distribution with mean 7.

(a) Use tables to find the probability, correct to three decimal places, that the number of incoming calls in an hour will be (i) exactly 7, (ii) more than 12, (iii) less than 5.

(b) Use tables to find the probability, correct to three decimal places, that in a period of two hours the number of incoming calls will be from 10 to 15, inclusive.

Solution

(a) Let X denote the number of incoming calls in one hour. We are given that $X \sim Po(7)$.

(i) $P(X = 7) \equiv P(X \leq 7) - P(X \leq 6)$
$$= 0.5987 - 0.4497 = 0.149 \text{ correct to three decimal places.}$$

(ii) $P(X > 12) \equiv 1 - P(X \leq 12) = 1 - 0.9730$
$$= 0.027 \text{ correct to three decimal places.}$$

(iii) $P(X < 5) \equiv P(X \leq 4) = 0.1730 = 0.173 \text{ correct to three decimal places.}$

(b) Let Y denote the number of incoming calls in a period of two hours. We know that $Y \sim Po(14)$.
$$P(10 \leq Y \leq 15) = P(Y \leq 15) - P(Y \leq 9) = 0.6694 - 0.1094$$
$$= 0.560 \text{ correct to three decimal places.}$$

Exercise 4.6b

1. Given that $X \sim Po(9)$, use tables to evaluate (a) $P(X = 9)$, (b) $P(X \leq 10)$, (c) $P(X > 12)$, (d) $P(7 \leq X \leq 13)$.

2. A dealer has a stock of six similar television sets available for weekly hire. The weekly demand for these sets has the Poisson distribution with mean 3.8. Find the probability, correct to three decimal places, that in a week (a) at least two of the sets will be hired, (b) the demand will exceed the supply.

3. The number of accidents occurring at a particular roundabout has a Poisson distribution, the average number per month being 6. Find, correct to three decimal places, the probability that there will be (a) more than 8 accidents in a month, (b) more than 6 accidents in two months, (c) from 8 to 16, inclusive, accidents in a period of two months.

4. The number of breakdowns in a day along a particular stretch of motorway has the Poisson distribution with mean 2.6. Use tables to find the smallest integer n if the probability of more than n breakdowns in a day is less than 0.04.

5. The number of misprints per page of a newspaper has the Poisson distribution with mean 3.8.

(a) Find the probability, correct to three decimal places, that a page will have more than 5 misprints.

(b) Find the smallest integer n if the probability of more than n misprints on a page is less than 0.1.

6. The random variable X has the Poisson distribution with mean μ. Show that

$$\sum_{x=0}^{r} xP(X = x) = \mu P(X \le r - 1).$$

The daily demand for a certain item at a particular shop has the Poisson distribution with mean 10.

(a) Use tables to find, correct to three decimal places, the probability that on a day the demand for the item will be (i) 21 or more, (ii) 19 or fewer.

(b) The shop receives delivery of the items every morning and accepts as many as are necessary to bring the stock level up to 20 items. The shop makes a profit of 50 p on each item sold. Show that the expected daily profit from the sale of these items is almost £5.

7. The number of cars passing over a bridge during a period of t minutes has the Poisson distribution with mean 0.2 t. Find, correct to 3 decimal places, the probability that

(a) in a period of 15 minutes, at least 4 cars will pass over the bridge.

(b) in a period of 1 hour, from 9 to 15 cars, inclusive, will pass over the bridge.

Mean and variance of Po(α)

If X ~ Po(α) then
$$E(X) = \alpha \text{ and } Var(X) = \alpha. \tag{3}$$

Proof:

$$P(X = x) = \frac{\alpha^x}{x!} e^{-\alpha} , \quad \text{for } x = 1, 2, 3, \cdots$$

$$E(X) = \sum_{x=0}^{\infty} \frac{x\alpha^x}{x!} e^{-\alpha} = e^{-\alpha} \sum_{x=1}^{\infty} \frac{\alpha^x}{(x-1)!}$$

$$= \alpha e^{-\alpha} \left\{ 1 + \alpha + \frac{\alpha^2}{2!} + \frac{\alpha^3}{3!} + \frac{\alpha^4}{4!} + \cdots \right\}$$

$$= \alpha e^{-\alpha} \times e^{\alpha} = \alpha.$$

$$E(X^2) = e^{-\alpha} \sum_{x=0}^{\infty} \frac{x^2 \alpha^x}{x!} = \alpha e^{-\alpha} \sum_{x=1}^{\infty} \frac{x\alpha^{x-1}}{(x-1)!}$$

$$= \alpha e^{-\alpha} \left[1 + 2\alpha + \frac{3\alpha^2}{2!} + \frac{4\alpha^3}{3!} + \cdots \right]$$

$$= \alpha e^{-\alpha} \left[\left\{ 1 + \alpha + \frac{\alpha^2}{2!} + \frac{\alpha^3}{3!} + \cdots \right\} + \left\{ \alpha + \frac{2\alpha^2}{2!} + \frac{3\alpha^3}{3!} + \cdots \right\} \right]$$

$$= \alpha e^{-\alpha} \left[e^{\alpha} + \alpha e^{\alpha} \right] = \alpha + \alpha^2$$

Since $E(X) = \alpha$,

$$\text{Var}(X) = E(X^2) - [E(X)]^2 = \alpha + \alpha^2 - \alpha^2 = \alpha.$$

Exercise 4.6c

1. The random variable X has the Poisson distribution with mean 4.8.
(a) Find the mean and the variance of (i) $3X - 2$, (ii) $15 - 2X$.
(b) Evaluate $E(2X^2 - 3X + 1)$.
2. The random variable X has the Poisson distribution whose standard deviation is 3. Evaluate, correct to three decimal places,
   (a) $P(X = 9)$, (b) $P(X \geq 9)$, (c) $P(5 \leq X \leq 11)$.
3. The number of times per day that a machine will require attention has the Poisson distribution with mean 1.5. The cost of running the machine on a day when it requires attention X times is $£(12 + 5X^2)$.

106

(a)   Calculate the expected daily cost of running the machine.

(b)   Find the probability that the cost of running the machine on a randomly chosen day will exceed £22.

4.7 Poisson approximation to the binomial

It can be shown that when n is large and p is small the binomial distribution B(n, p) may be approximated by the Poisson distribution having mean $\mu = np$ (equal to the mean of the binomial distribution). The larger the value of n and the smaller the value of p the better the approximation. This approximation can be particularly useful when n is larger than the largest value given in binomial tables (say greater than 50) and p is small (say < 0.1). The following table, in which $X \sim B(n, p)$, illustrates the approximation for some selected values of n and p.

n	p	$P(X \leq 3)$	$\mu = np$	Poisson approx
50	0.02	0.9822	1	0.9810
50	0.01	0.9984	0.5	0.9982
100	0.02	0.8590	2	0.8571
100	0.01	0.9816	1	0.9810
500	0.004	0.8575	2	0.8572

Example 1

A manufactured item has probability 0.003 of being defective. The items are boxed in cartons, each containing 1000 of the items. Purchasers of these cartons will return any carton that contains 3 or more defective items. Use a Poisson approximation to calculate

(a)   the proportion of cartons that will not be returned,

(b)   the conditional probability that a carton that has not been returned contains no defective item.

Solution

Let X denote the number of defective items in a carton. Then X has the binomial distribution B(1000, 0.003). Since n is very large and p is very small we can approximate this distribution by the distribution of Y, where $Y \sim Po(\mu)$ with $\mu = np = 3$.

(a)   The proportion of cartons that will not be returned is

$$P(X \leq 2) \approx P(Y \leq 2) = e^{-3}\left(1 + 3 + \frac{3^2}{2!}\right) = 8.5e^{-3} = 0.423, \text{ correct to three decimal places.}$$

(b)   The required conditional probability is

P(no defective in carton| carton not returned) = P(X = 0|X ≤ 2)

$$= \frac{P(X=0)}{P(X\le 2)} \approx \frac{P(Y=0)}{P(Y\le 2)} = \frac{e^{-3}}{8.5e^{-3}} = \frac{2}{17} = 0.118, \text{ correct to three decimal places.}$$

The following example shows how a Poisson approximation may be used when n is large and p is close to 1.

Example 2

In Example 1 above use a Poisson approximation to calculate the probability that a carton will contain at least 995 nondefective items.

Solution

Since the probability of an item being defective is 0.003, the probability of an item being nondefective is 0.997. Let W denote the number of nondefective items in a carton of 1000 items. Then W ~ B(1000, 0.997). We are required to evaluate P(W ≥ 995). On noting that W = 1000 – X, where X is as defined in Example 1, it follows that

P(W ≥ 995) ≡ P(X ≤ 5).

Using Y ~ Po(3) as an approximation to the distribution of X we have

P(W ≥ 995) ≡ P(X ≤ 5) ≈ P(Y ≤ 5) = 0.916 correct to 3 decimal places.

Exercise 2.7

1.   Given that X ~ B(150, 0.04), find approximate values for (a) P(X ≤ 3), (b) P(X = 5),
      (c) P(X > 4) .

2.   The probability that a mass-produced item will be defective is 0.002. The items are packed in boxes, each box containing 500 items. Using an appropriate distributional approximation find, correct to three decimal places, the probability that a box will contain (a) exactly two defective items, (b) at least three defective items.

3.   It has been estimated that 0.7% of women have a certain disease. Find, approximately, the probability that in a group of 400 women no more than five have the disease.

4.   The probability of a baby being stillborn is 0.0001. Find the probability that of the next 5000 births (a) none will be stillborn, (b) exactly one will be stillborn, (c) at least two will be stillborn.

5.   An aeroplane has 196 seats. Past experience has shown that 1.5% of passengers who have booked flights fail to turn up. If the airline sells 200 tickets for a particular flight,

find approximate values for the probability that (a) more than 196 turn up, (b) the flight will have one or more empty seats.

6. A certain make of television has a maintenance-free guarantee for four years. The makers are confident that 99.6% of its televisions will operate trouble-free for four years. In a consignment of 200 televisions, find approximate values for the probabilities that (a) none will need any maintenance during the guarantee period, (b) at least 197 of them will not require maintenance during the guarantee period.

7. The probability that a mass produced item will be defective is 0.01. Find approximate values for the probabilities that in a random sample of 200 items

(a) exactly 3 will be defective,

(b) at most 2 will be defective,

(c) at least 3 will be defective.

Miscellaneous Questions on Chapter 4

1. (1987) The demand per week for videos in a particular shop has the Poisson distribution with mean 4.

(i) Find, to four decimal places, the probabilities that in a week the demand for videos at the shop will be (a) exactly 2, (b) 5 or fewer.

(ii) Videos are delivered to the shop at the beginning of each week only, and the policy is to accept as many as are required for the stock level to be 5. Show that the most probable number of videos that will be *sold* in a week is 5, and find, to two decimal places, the expected number of videos that will be *sold* in a week. [11]

2. (1987) A self-service cafeteria offers only two main courses, A and B, at lunchtime. Experience has shown that 60% of the customers opt for A.

(i) Calculate the probabilities that on any day (a) exactly 3 of the first 6 customers will opt for A, (b) the fourth customer will be the first to opt for B. [3]

(ii) Use tables to find the probability that of the first 10 customers on any day, 7 or fewer will opt for A. [2]

(iii) On a particular day only 30 servings of A and 25 servings of B are available. Use tables to find the probabilities that of the first 50 customers on that day, (a) every one will be able to have the course of his/her choice, (b) the number opting for A will be at least twice the number opting for B. [6]

3. (1988) In each trial of a random experiment, the probability that the event A will occur is 0.6. In eight independent trials of the experiment calculate, correct to four decimal

places, the probabilities that (a) A will occur in exactly five of the trials, (b) A will occur in exactly five trials, these trials being consecutive. [4]

4. (1988) Independently on each day, the number of times that a machine will require attention has the Poisson distribution with mean 1.2. Find, correct to three decimal places, the probabilities that (i) on any day, the machine will require attention exactly three times, (ii) on two successive days, the machine will require attention twice on one of the days and once on the other day. [4]

    The cost of running the machine on a day when it requires attention X times is £$(12 + 10X^2)$. Find the expected daily cost of running the machine. [4]

5. (1989) The random variable X has the following distribution.

x	1	2	3
P(X = x)	α	$0.8 - \alpha$	0.2

    Given that the mean of the distribution is equal to 1.7, determine the value of α. [3]

6. (1990) Independently for each page of a printed book the number of errors occurring has a Poisson distribution with mean 0.2. Find, correct to three decimal places, the probabilities that (i) the first page will contain no error, (ii) four of the first five pages will contain no error, (iii) the first error will occur on the third page.

    [5]

7. (1990) Two machines A and B are used to produce identical items. Independently for each item produced on machine A the probability that it is defective is 0.01, while for an item produced on machine B the corresponding probability is 0.03.

(a) Three items are chosen at random from those produced on machine A and three items are chosen at random from those produced on machine B. (i) Calculate the probability that exactly one of the three items produced on machine A is defective. (ii) Calculate, correct to three decimal places, the probability that exactly one of the six chosen items is defective. [4]

(b) Of the total output of items produced in a day, 60% are produced on machine A and 40% are produced on machine B. (i) If one item is chosen at random from a day's output, show that the probability of it being nondefective is 0.982. (iii) A box contains 80 items chosen at random from a day's output. Find an approximate value for the probability that the box contains at most two defective items. [6]

8. (1991) Independently for each seed of a particular variety of flower that is sown, the probability that the seed will germinate is 0.8. (i) Twenty such seeds are sown. Use

tables to find the probability that the number that will germinate lies between 14 and 18, inclusive. [3]

9. (1991) Independently for each page, the number of typing errors per page in the first draft of a novel has a Poisson distribution with mean 0.4.

(a) Calculate, correct to five decimal places, the probabilities that (i) a randomly chosen page will contain no error, (ii) a randomly chosen page will contain two or more errors, (iii) the third of three randomly chosen pages will be the first to contain an error. [5]

(b) Write down an expression for the probability that each of n randomly chosen pages will contain no error. Hence find the largest n for which there is a probability of at least 0.1 that each of the n pages contains no error. [3]

Independently for each page, the number, Y, of typing errors per page in the first draft of a Mathematics textbook also has a Poisson distribution.

(c) Given that $P(Y = 2) = 2P(Y = 3)$,
(i) find $E(Y)$, (ii) show that $P(Y = 5) = 4P(Y = 6)$. [4]

(d) One page is chosen at random from the first draft of the novel and one page is chosen at random from the first draft of the Mathematics textbook. Calculate, correct to three decimal places, the probability that exactly one of the two chosen pages will contain no error. [3]

10. (1992) A loaded die is such that when it is thrown the probability of obtaining a score of 6 is 0.25. In five independent throws of the die calculate, correct to three decimal places, the probabilities that a 6 will be obtained (i) exactly once, (ii) for the first time on the fifth throw, (iii) for the second time on the fifth throw. [7]

11. (1993) The random variable X has the distribution given in the following table.

x	0	1	2
$P(X = x)$	$0.4 - 0.5\alpha$	α	$0.6 - 0.5\alpha$

Given that the standard deviation of X is 0.8, find the value of α. [4]

12. (1993) The probability that a patient suffering from a particular disease will be cured following treatment is 0.97.

(a) If the treatment is given to 10 patients find, correct to three decimal places, the probability that exactly 8 of them will be cured.

(b) If the treatment is given to 24 patients calculate, correct to three decimal places, the probability that at least 22 of them will be cured.

(c)   If the treatment is given to 64 patients, use a Poisson approximation to calculate the probability that at least 62 of them will be cured; give your answer correct to three decimal places. [8]

The treatment is to be given to 5 patients at Hospital A and to 3 patients at Hospital B.

(d)   Calculate, correct to three decimal places, the probability that of the 5 patients treated at Hospital A the first, second, fourth, and fifth to be treated will be cured but the third will not be cured. [2]

(e)   Given that 6 of the patients treated at the two hospitals were cured, calculate the conditional probability that 4 of the cured patients were treated at Hospital A. [5]

13.   (1994) Two unbiased cubical dice are thrown simultaneously. Calculate the probability that (i) the scores on both dice are at least 3, (ii) the scores on the two dice differ by 2.

[4]

14.   (1994) The random variable X has the binomial distribution B(n, p). Using tables, and where necessary an appropriate distributional approximation, find $P(X \geq 6)$ and $P(X = 6)$ in the two cases (i) $n = 20$, $p = 0.4$, (ii) $n = 200$, $p = 0.04$. [5]

15.   (1994) The number of telephone calls arrriving at a certain office in a period of duration t hours has a Poisson distribution with mean 12t. (i) Find the probability that there are 4 calls in a half hour period. (iii) Find the probability that there are 5 calls between 10.00 am and 10.30 am, given that there are 12 calls between 10.00 am and 11.30 am. [7]

16.   (1995) A manufacturer of wine glasses knows from his records that 1% of glasses passed for sale are actually defective.

(a)   The manager of a large store decides to sell the glasses in presentation boxes containing 12 glasses. (i) Calculate, correct to four decimal places, the probability that a box contains no defective glasses. (ii) Calculate the probability that, in a batch of 10 boxes, at least 9 of the boxes contain no defective glasses. [3]

(b)   A wholesaler buys 1500 glasses. Use the Poisson distribution to find, approximately, the probability that no more than 10 of these are defective. [3]

17.   (1995) A confectioner bakes 3 fruit cakes every day. She knows from past experience that the demand per day for these cakes is a Poisson random variable with mean 2.5.

(a)   Without using tables calculate, correct to four decimal places, the probabilities of selling 0, 1, 2 cakes, respectively, on a particular day.

(b)   Deduce the probability of selling 3 cakes on a particular day. [5]

(c)   Calculate the mean number of cakes sold per day. [2]

Each cake costs £1.50 to make and sells for £5.

(d)   Calculate the mean profit per day from the sales of these cakes.   [2]

The confectioner considers the possibility of increasing her daily output to 4 fruit cakes.

(i) If she does this, calculate the mean profit per day from the sale of these cakes.

(ii) Would you advise her to increase her output to 4 fruit cakes per day?   [6]

18.   (S1 Jan 1996) The owner of a hotel decides to sell copies of the local morning paper, the *Gazette*, to his guests. Assuming that he has n guests and that each guest independently wants to buy the *Gazette* with probability p, state the probability distribution that should be used to model the total number of guests wanting to buy the *Gazette*. One morning, he has 20 guests and he decides to buy 4 copies of the *Gazette* for re-sale. Assume that p = 0.16.

(a)   Calculate, correct to four decimal places, the probabilities that he sells 0, 1, 2, 3 copies of the *Gazette*. (b) **Deduce** the probability that he sells all 4 copies.   [7]

(c)   Each copy costs him 20p and sells for 50p; unsold copies have to be thrown away. Calculate, correct to the nearest penny, his expected profit from the sales of the *Gazette*.

    [4]

19.   (A3 1996) A gardener plants 20 seeds in a tray. Each seed germinates with probability 0·45, independently of all other seeds. Use the tables provided to find the probability that the number of seeds which germinate

(a) is at least 15, (b) is exactly 15.   [3]

20.   (S1 June 1996) In a large Welsh school, 65% of the pupils speak Welsh. A random sample of 20 pupils from the school is taken.

(a) State the name of a probability distribution that can be used to model the number of Welsh speakers in the sample.   [1]

(b) Use your model to find the probability that at least 12 pupils in the sample speak Welsh.

    [2]

(c) Given that there are at least 12 Welsh speakers in the sample, find the probability that there are no more than 15 Welsh speakers in the sample.   [4]

21.   (S1 June 1996) Three unbiased coins are tossed simultaneously and those coins falling heads are simultaneously tossed again. The total number of heads obtained in the two tossings is denoted by X.

(a) Using a tree diagram, or otherwise, show that

$$P(X = 6) = \frac{1}{64} \quad \text{and} \quad P(X = 3) = \frac{13}{64} \,.$$

    [3]

(b) Find the probability distribution of X.   [4]

(c) Calculate E(X).   [2]

22. (S1 June 1996) Faults occur at random in the manufacture of a certain cable at a mean rate of 3·75 per 100 m. Lengths of the cable are wound onto drums carrying 40 m. If X represents the number of faults occurring on a drum, write down an appropriate model for the distribution of X. [1]

(a) Find, without using tables, the probability that there are at least 2 faults on a drum. [2]

(b) A customer buys 5 drums. Find the probability that exactly 3 of them have at least 2 faults. [2]

NUMERICAL ANSWERS

Exercise 1.2

1. *Method 2:* 6, 12, 14, 21, 22, 24, 28, 30   *Method 3:* 6, 9, 13, 14, 21, 22, 28, 30

2. *Both methods:* 4, 5, 14, 29, 32, 35, 37, 62, 71, 77

3. *Method 2:* 5, 37, 45, 50, 109   *Method 3:* 1, 39, 61, 71, 109

4. *Method 2:* 4, 48, 51, 126, 130, 149   *Method 3:* 44, 67, 73, 94, 113, 115

5. *Method 2:* 51, 504, 906, 1028, 1263, 1308, 1935, 2090, 2937, 3172
   Method 3: 51, 307, 504, 1263, 1308, 1577, 1935, 2804, 2937, 3172

Exercise 1.3

1. (a) 14 Year 12, 10 Year 13 ;   (b) 1, 8, 9, 10, 11, 12, 14, 17, 19, 21, 24, 29, 30, 32

3. 57, 46, 17

Exercise 2.1

1. Mean = $42\frac{8}{11}$, Median = 42, Range = 15, IQR = 6

2. Mean = 2·575, Median = 2, Range = 4, IQR = 3

3. (b) (i) 166·5 cm   (ii) 5·1 cm ;   (c) 166·8 cm

Exercise 2.2

1. 5, 1·789   2. 167·857 cm, 5·167 cm   3. 19·2 mm, 1·166 mm

4. 50, 15·067   5. 40·2 wpm, 2·441 wpm   6. 0·85 s, 2·853 s

7. (a) B ; (b) A ; (c) B (larger mean, smaller SD)

8. 29, 5·9   9. (a) 34 , (b) 19·227   10. $a = 4$, $b = 6$

Exercise 2.3

1. 1·467, 1·024   2. 2·88, 1·291   3. 2·1, 0·995   4. 53·058, 1·574

5. 1·1, 1·068   6. 2·98, 1·691   7. 7·667, 0·645   8. 3·16, 2·092

Exercise 2.4

1. 31·96 y, 10·208 y   2. 79·2, 3·201   3. 27120 km, 10386 km

4. 209·517 g, 36·592 g   5. 7·494, 3·718

6. *Town:* 39·3 y, 20·156 y; *Resort:* 51·9 y, 18·361 y

Exercise 2.6

1. 30 y, 13 y   2. 79·1, 7·4   3. 14·8 th.km   4. 206·3 g, 205·1 g

5. 7 kg, 5·7 kg   6. *Town:* 38 y, 29·8 y ; *Resort:* 54 y, 28·9 y

Miscellaneous questions on Chapter 2

1. Mode = 6, median = 6, Mean = 6·28, IQR = 3, SD = 1·96

2. (a) Median = 2, IQR = 2;   (b) Mean = 2·05, SD = 1·23

3. (a) Mean = 24·43 g, SD = 7·67 g ;   (b) Median = 24·3 g , IQR = 10 g

4. (b) Median = 2·64 kg, Mean = 2·64 kg

5. (a) Mean = 19y 1m;   (b) Median = 21y 0m, 10-90 interpercentile range = 3y 3m

6. (b) Median = 18·57y, IQR = 8·6y ;   (c) 13·33y ;   (d) 13·5y

Exercise 3.1

1. [0, 1, 2, 3, 4]   **2.** [0, 1, 2, 3, 4, 5, 6]   **3.** [1, 2, 3, 4]

4. [(WW), (WR), (RW), (RR)]

5. (a) [(HHH), (HHT), (HTH), (THH), (HTT), (THT), (TTH), (TTT)], (b) [0, 1, 2, 3]

6. [1, 2, 3, 4, . . .]

Exercise 3.2

1. (a) S = [1, 2, 3, 4, 5, 6], A = [2, 4, 6], B = [1, 2], C = [3, 6], B and C;

(b)(i) [1, 3, 5] (ii) [2] (iii) [1, 2,4, 5, 6] (iv) [1, 2, 3,4, 6] (v) [6].

2. [(x, y) : x, y = 1,2,3,4,5,6]

(a) A = [(1,3), (2,2), (3,1), (2,6), (3,5), (4,4), (5,3), (6,2), (6,6)]

(b) B = [(1,1), (2,2), (3,3), (4,4), (5,5), (6,6)]

(c) C = [(2,2), (2,4), (2,6), (4,2), (4,4), (4,6), (6,2), (6,4), (6,6)]

(d) D = [(1,5), (1,6), (2,6), (5,1), (6,1), (6,2)]   (e) [(2,2), (2,6), (4,4), (6,2), (6,6)]

(f) [(1,1), (1,5), (1,6), (2,2), (2,6), (3,3), (4,4), (5,1), (5,5), (6,1), (6,2), (6,6)]

(g) [(1,1), (3,3), (5,5)], B and D.

3. (a) [8, 9], (b) [3, 5, 7], (c) [3, 5, 7, 9] (d) [3, 5, 7, 8, 9] (e) [3, 5, 7] (f) [8, 9]

(g) [4, 6] (h) [3, 5, 7].

Exercise 3.3

1. (a) 0.3 (b) 0.8 (c) 0.6   **2.** (a) 0.6 (b) 0.4 (c) 1

3. (a) 0.12 (b) 0.18 (c) 0.72   **4.** (a) 0.75 (b) 0.5 (c) 0.5 (d) 0.1 (e) 0.25

5. (a) 0.64 (b) 0.12 (c) 0.13 (d) 0.37   **6.** (a) 0.12 (b) 0.4 (c) 0.72 (d) 0.28

7. (a) $\frac{5}{6}$ (b) $\frac{1}{3}$ (c) $\frac{1}{3}$ (d) $\frac{11}{12}$.

Exercise 3.4a

1. (a) $\frac{4}{13}$, (b) $\frac{15}{36}$, (c) $\frac{3}{13}$, (d) $\frac{5}{13}$, (e) $\frac{1}{13}$ **2.** $\frac{7}{20}$

3. (a) $\frac{2}{9}$, (b) $\frac{5}{9}$, (c) $\frac{1}{3}$ **4.** (a)(i) $\frac{5}{36}$, (ii) $\frac{1}{6}$, (b) $\frac{1}{6}$, (c) $\frac{2}{9}$.

Exercise 3.4b

1. (a) $\frac{1}{13}$ (b) $\frac{25}{169}$ **2.** (a) $\frac{1}{9}$ (b) $\frac{7}{27}$ **3.** 5 (assuming birthmonths equally likely)

4. (a) $\frac{5}{9}$ (b) $\frac{1}{9}$ **5.** (a) $\frac{29}{118}$ (b) $\frac{10}{59}$ (c) $\frac{33}{59}$ **6.** (a) $\frac{1}{4}$ (b) $\frac{1}{6}$ (c) $\frac{5}{9}$

7. (i)(a) $\frac{6}{25}$ (b) $\frac{7}{225}$ (ii) (a) $\frac{9}{35}$ (b) $\frac{1}{35}$ **8.** (a) $\frac{1}{4}$ (b) $\frac{3}{8}$ (c) $\frac{3}{16}$

Exercise 3.4c

1. (a) $\dfrac{1}{22}$ (b) $\dfrac{3}{44}$ (c) $\dfrac{37}{44}$　　2. (a) $\dfrac{1}{14}$ (b) $\dfrac{3}{7}$ (c) $\dfrac{19}{42}$

3. (a) $\dfrac{3}{14}$ (b) $\dfrac{1}{7}$ (c) $\dfrac{18}{35}$　　4. (a) $\dfrac{1}{5525}$ (b) $\dfrac{6}{5525}$ (c) $\dfrac{16}{5525}$

5. $\dfrac{17}{33}$　　6. (a) $\dfrac{7}{15}$ (b) $\dfrac{1}{15}$　　7. (a) $\dfrac{676}{4921}$ (b) $\dfrac{2}{191919}$ (c) $\dfrac{690}{4921}$

8. (a) $\dfrac{1}{132}$ (b) $\dfrac{25}{66}$ (c) $\dfrac{1}{2}$

Exercise 3.5

1. $\dfrac{2}{3}$　2. $\dfrac{1}{2}$　3. (a) $\dfrac{1}{7}$ (b) $\dfrac{1}{4}$　4. (a) $\dfrac{2}{3}$ (b) $\dfrac{2}{5}$ (c) $\dfrac{1}{3}$ (d) $\dfrac{4}{7}$

5. $\dfrac{3}{20}$　6. (a) $\dfrac{3}{11}$ (b) $\dfrac{3}{7}$　7. (a) $\dfrac{5}{6}$ (b) $\dfrac{3}{10}$　8. (a) $\dfrac{10}{21}$ (b) $\dfrac{6}{7}$

9. $\dfrac{1}{2}$　10. (a) $\dfrac{1}{2}$ (b) $\dfrac{5}{17}$ (c) $\dfrac{10}{13}$

Exercise 3.6

1. (a) $\dfrac{1}{13}$ (b) $\dfrac{1}{17}$　2. (a) 0.0225 (b) A　3. $\dfrac{8}{23}$

4. (a)(i) $\dfrac{19}{135}$ (ii) $\dfrac{13}{27}$ (b) C　5. (a) $\dfrac{8}{23}$ (b) $\dfrac{9}{23}$ (c) $\dfrac{6}{23}$　6. $\dfrac{7}{50}$

7. $\dfrac{19}{118}$　8. $\dfrac{21}{50}$　9. (a) 0.32 (b) 0.5625

10. $\dfrac{25}{63}$　12. $\dfrac{1}{3}$

Exercise 3.7

1. (a) $\dfrac{119}{120}$ (b) $\dfrac{5}{12}$　2. (a) 0.7 (b) 0.66　3. (a) $\dfrac{11}{850}$ (b) $\dfrac{39}{850}$ (c) $\dfrac{169}{425}$

4. (a) $\dfrac{17}{48}$ (b)(i) $\dfrac{3}{23}$ (ii) $\dfrac{5}{23}$　5. (a) $\dfrac{11}{21}$ (b) $\dfrac{6}{11}$　6. (a) 0.027 (b) $\dfrac{291}{973}$

7. (a) $\dfrac{11}{20}$ (b) $\dfrac{5}{33}$

Exercise 3.8a

1. (a) 0.2 (b) 0.7　2. Independent　3. Independent　5. 0.3, 0.2

7. Independent　9. A, B and A, C　10. (b) 6

Exercise 3.8b

1. 0.58　2. (a) 0.25 (b) 0.75　3. 0.9519

4. (a)(i) 0.429875 (ii) 0.1987 (b) 13, 9, 6　5. (a) 0.504 (b) 0.398

6. 0.59375　7. (a) $\dfrac{5}{36}$ (b) $\dfrac{125}{1296}$ (c) $\dfrac{1}{6}\left(\dfrac{5}{6}\right)^{2n-1}$; $\dfrac{5}{11}$

Miscellaneous questions on Chapter 3

1. (i) not independent (ii) $\dfrac{1}{4}$ **3.** (ii)(a) $\dfrac{11}{24}$ (b) $\dfrac{8}{11}$ **4.** (ii) 0.48, 0.6

5. (i) $\dfrac{1}{2}$ (ii) $\dfrac{7}{15}$ **6.** (a)(i) $\dfrac{49}{143}$ (ii) $\dfrac{7}{16}$ (b)(iii) $\dfrac{7}{20}$ **7.** (i) 0.7 (ii) 0.2 (iii) 0.6

8. (i) $\dfrac{2}{7}$ (ii) $\dfrac{5}{84}$ (iii) $\dfrac{30}{79}$ **9.** (ii) 0.478   **10.** (b)(i) 0.3 (ii) $\dfrac{2}{3}$

11. (i) 0.25 (ii) 0.48 (iii) 0.292   **12.** (i) $\dfrac{1}{14}$ (ii) $\dfrac{3}{7}$ **13.** (i) 0.017 (ii) $\dfrac{25}{97}$

14. (a) 0.4 (b) 0.9   **15.** (i) $\dfrac{4}{9}$ (ii) $\dfrac{2}{9}$ **16.** (i) $\dfrac{3}{5}$ (ii) $\dfrac{4}{9}$

17. (a)(ii) $\dfrac{196}{295}$ (b) 0.6528   **18.** (i) $\dfrac{7}{15}$ **19.** $\dfrac{97}{105}$

20. (a) $\dfrac{3}{8}$ (b) $\dfrac{1}{2}$ (c) $\dfrac{2}{5}$ **21.** (a) not independent (b) $\dfrac{1}{3}$ **22.** (a) 0.0382 (b) 0.746

23. (b) 0.4   **24.** (a)(i) 0.12 (ii) 0.46   **25.** (a) 1/4845 (b) 48/323

Exercise 4.1

1. 0, 1, 2   **2.** 0, 1, 2, 3, 4   **3.** 0, 1, 2, . . ., 12   **4.** 1, 2, 3, 4, 5, 6

5. 0, 1, 2, 3, . . .   **6.** 1, 2, 3, . . .

Exercise 4.2

1.

x	0	1	2
P(X = x)	25/36	10/36	1/36

2.

x	0	1	2	3
P(X = x)	84/220	108/220	27/220	1/220

3.

x	0	1	2
P(X = x)	0.9801	0.0198	0.0001

4.

	x	0	1	2	3
(a)	P(X = x)	969/2024	855/2024	190/2024	10/2024
(b)	P(X = x)	6859/13824	5415/13824	1425/13824	125/13824

5. $\dfrac{1}{5}$

6.

x	6	7	8	9	10	11	12	13
P(X = x)	20/165	45/165	18/165	31/165	36/165	6/165	6/165	3/165

7. $P(X = x) = 0.4(0.6)^{x-1}$, x = 1, 2, 3, . . .

8.

x	0	1	2
P(X = x)	19/160	74/160	67/160

9.

	x	1	2	3	4
(a)	P(X = x)	1/4	3/16	9/64	27/64
(b)	P(X = x)	1/4	1/4	1/4	1/4
(c)	P(X = x)	1/4	1/4	1/6	1/3

Exercise 4.3a

1. (a) $5\frac{1}{6}$ (b) 0.22 (c) 2 (d) 2.7 (e) 2.08 **2.** $\frac{1}{4}$ **3.** 0.75 pence **5.** 2

6. $1\frac{1}{2}$ **7.** (a) $1\frac{4}{5}$ **8.** 1.6 **9.** 4

Exercise 4.3b

3. $\frac{1}{2}$ **4.** (a) $\frac{24}{11}$ (b) $\frac{61}{11}$ (c) $\frac{61}{11}$ **5.** (b) 13.5 **6.** (a) 47 (b) 2.4 **7.** $1\frac{1}{2}$

Exercise 4.4a

1. (a) 2.2, 0.748 (b) 2.4, 1.2 (c) 13.75, 4.84 (d) 3.54, 0.684

2. (a) $1, \frac{1}{2}$ (b) $1\frac{3}{7}, \frac{45}{98}$ **3.** 4.4, 0.44 **4.** 5.25, 3.22 **5.** 440.74

Exercise 4.4b

1. (a) 11, 2 (b) 20, 4 (c) 25, 6 (d) $-19, 4$ (e) 4, 1

2. $a = -\frac{1}{4}, b = 2$ or $a = \frac{1}{4}, b = -2$ **3.** £415.20, £177.60 **4.** 0.9, 0.7 ; 4.8, 1.4

5. 60, 20 **6.** 3.5, 1.25 (a) 6, 5 (b) 1, 5 **7.** 4, 36

Exercise 4.5a

1. (a)(i) 0.276 (ii) 0.456 (b)(i) 0.254 (ii) 0.448 **2.** (a) 0.044 (b) 0.055 (c) 0.989 (d) 0.945 **3.** 0.196, 0 or 1 **4.** (a) $\frac{3}{8}$ (b) $\frac{7}{8}$ (c) $\frac{1}{2}$

5. (a) $\frac{1701}{8192}$ (b) $\frac{277}{65536}$ **6.** (a) $\frac{80}{243}$ (b) $\frac{112}{243}$ **7.** (a) $\frac{945}{16384}$ (b) $\frac{289}{4096}$

8. (a) 0.200 (b) 0.383 **9.** $\frac{5}{16}$ **10.** (a)(i) 2 (ii) 1 and 2

Exercise 4.5b

1. (a) 0.061 (b) 0.383 (c) 0.581 (d) 0.763

2. (a) 0.008 (b) 0.156 (c) 0.763 (d) 0.231

3. 0.881 **4.** (a) 0.630 (b) 0.474

5. (a) 0.117 (b) 0.244 **6.** (a) 0.119 (b) 0.830

7. (i)(a) 0.088 (b) 0.967 (ii)(a) 0.124 (b) 0.874 **8.** 0.089

Exercise 4.5c

1. $\dfrac{2}{3}, \dfrac{5}{9}$ 2. (a) $\dfrac{1}{4}$ (b) $2\dfrac{1}{2}$ (c) $\dfrac{295245}{1048576}$ 3. 4   4. 6.4

5. 5, 5.07   6. 20, 16 ; 200, 20

Exercise 4.6a

1. (a) 0.224 (b) 0.423 (c) 0.185 2. (a) 0.156 (b) 0.469

3. (a) 0.135 (b) 0.947   4. (a)(i) 0.175 (ii) 0.265 (b) 0.038

5. (a) 0.214 (b) 0.456   6. (a) 0.879 (b) 0.221   7. 0.010

8. (a) $e^{-4}, 4e^{-4}, 8e^{-4}, \dfrac{32}{3}e^{-4}, \dfrac{32}{3}e^{-4}, 1 - \dfrac{103}{3}e^{-4}$; 13.59 (b) £3.94 (c) No

Exercise 4.6b

1. (a) 0.132 (b) 0.706 (c) 0.124 (d) 0.719   2. (a) 0.893 (b) 0.091

3. (a) 0.153 (b) 0.954 (c) 0.809   4. 6   5. (a) 0.184 (b) 6

6. (a)(i) 0.002 (ii) 0.997 (b) £7.11   7. (a) 0.353 (b) 0.689

Exercise 4.6c

1. (a)(i) 12.4, 43.2 (ii) 5.4, 19.2 (b) 42.28

2. (a) 0.132 (b) 0.544 (c) 0.748   3. (a) £30.75 (b) 0.4422 to 4 d.p.

Exercise 4.7

1. (a) 0.151 (b) 0.161 (c) 0.715   2. (a) 0.184 (b) 0.080   3. 0.935

4. (a) 0.607 (b) 0.303 (c) 0.090   5. (a) 0.647 (b) 0.185

6. (a) 0.449 (b) 0.991   7. (a) 0.180 (b) 0.677 (c) 0.323

Miscellaneous questions on Chapter 4

1. (i)(a) 0.1465 (b) 0.7851 (ii) 3.59

2. (i)(a) 0.27648 (b) 0.0864 (ii) 0.8327 (iii)(a) 0.4962 (b) 0.1561

3. (a) 0.2787 (b) 0.0199   4. (i) 0.087 (ii) 0.157 (iii) £38.40

5. 0.5   6. (i) 0.819 (ii) 0.407 (iii) 0.122

7. (a)(i) 0.029403 (ii) 0.109 (b)(ii) 0.478 (iii) 0.825   8. (i) 0.8441

9. (a)(i) 0.67032 (ii) 0.06155 (iii) 0.14813 (b) 5 (c)(i) 1.5 (d) 0.594

10. (i) 0.396 (ii) 0.079 (iii) 0.105

11. 0.32   12. (a) 0.032 (b) 0.966 (c) 0.698 (d) 0.027 (e) 15/28

13. (i) $\dfrac{4}{9}$ (ii) $\dfrac{2}{9}$ 14. (i) 0.1244 (ii) 0.1222

15. (i) 0.1339 to 4 d.p. (ii) 0.1908 to 4 d.p.

16. (a)(i) 0.8864 (ii) 0.6832 (b) 0.1185

17. (a) 0.0821, 0.2052, 0.2565 (b) 0.4562 (c) 2.087 (d) £5.93 (i) £5.65 (ii) No

18. (a) 0.0306, 0.1165, 0.2109, 0.2410 (b) 0.4010 (c) 63 pence

19. (a) 0.0064 (b) 0.0049 20. (b) 0.7624 (c) 0.845 21. (c) 2.25

22. (a) 0.4422 (b) 0.2690

INDEX